Dinah Zike's
Reading and Study Skills
for Health

FOLDABLES™

Mc Graw Hill **Glencoe**

New York, New York   Columbus, Ohio   Chicago, Illinois   Woodland Hills, California

Glencoe

The *McGraw·Hill* Companies

Printed in the United States of America.

Send all inquiries to:
Glencoe/McGraw-Hill
21600 Oxnard Street, Suite 500
Woodland Hills, California 91367

ISBN-13: 978-0-07-875577-4
ISBN-10: 0-07-875577-8

4 5 6 7 8 9   079   11 10 09 08

Table of Contents

Introduction to Foldables

Folding Instructions

Foldables Chapter Activities
for *Teen Health*

The pages that follow contain chapter-specific Foldables activities to use with *Teen Health*. Included are a Chapter Summary, a Chapter Preview reproduction of the Foldables Study Organizer that appears on each chapter opener in the textbooks, and a Foldables Follow-Up Activity. Use the Follow-Up Activity after students have studied each chapter. Students are asked to use the Foldables they have created and completed during the study of each chapter to review important chapter concepts and prepare for the chapter test.

Alternative Foldables activities are also included for every chapter. Use these activities during the study of each chapter or as chapter review activities. The Student Study Tip provides reading, writing, and test-taking strategies that you can share with your students throughout the program.

Course 1

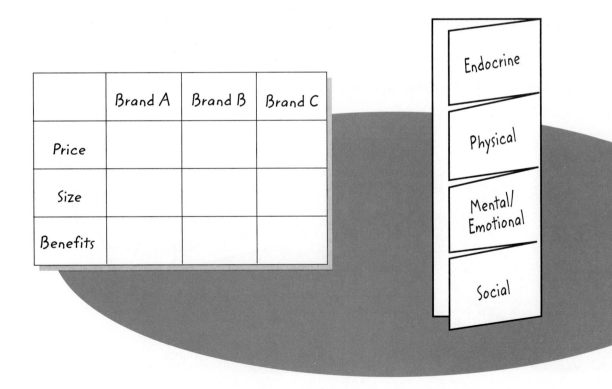

Course 2

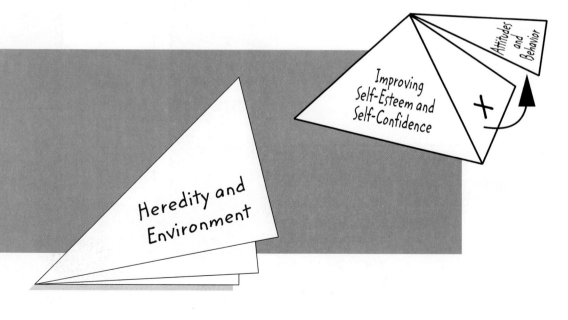

Course 3

Protect the Environment

Reduce   Reuse   Recycle

What's a Foldable?

A Foldable is a three-dimensional, student-made, interactive graphic organizer based on a skill. Making a Foldable gives students a fast, kinesthetic activity that helps them organize and retain information. Every chapter in the Student Edition of the textbook begins with a Foldable that is used as a study organizer. Each chapter's Foldable is designed to be used as a study guide for the main ideas and key points presented in the chapter. Foldables can also be used for a more in-depth investigation of a concept, idea, opinion, event, or person or place studied in a chapter. The purpose of this ancillary is to show you how to create various types of Foldables and provide chapter-specific Foldables examples. With this information, you can individualize Foldables to meet your curriculum needs.

This book is divided into two sections. The first section presents step-by-step instructions, illustrations, and photographs of 34 Foldables, many of which are not used in the Student Edition. I've included over 100 photographs to help you visualize how the Foldables might enhance instruction. The second section presents additional ideas on how to use Foldables for each chapter in the textbook. You can use the instructions section to design your own Foldables or alter the Foldables presented in each chapter. I recommend making this book available as a source for students who wish to learn new and creative ways to make study guides, present projects, or do extra-credit work.

Some of the Foldables featured in this book have been used in supplemental programs or staff development workshops. Today my Foldables are used internationally. I present workshops and keynote addresses to over 50,000 teachers and parents each year, sharing Foldables that I began inventing, designing, and adapting over 35 years ago. Students of all ages are using them for daily work, note-taking activities, student-directed projects, forms of alternative assessment, journals, graphs, charts, tables, and more.

Have fun using and adapting Foldables!

Why Use Foldables in Health?

When teachers ask me why they should take the time to use the Foldables featured in this book, I explain that Foldables

- quickly organize, display, and arrange data, making it easier for students to grasp health studies concepts, theories, facts, opinions, questions, research, and ideas.

- help sequence events as outlined in the content standards.

- result in study guides that the students compile as they listen for main ideas, read for main ideas, or conduct research.

- provide a multitude of creative formats in which students can present projects, research, interviews, and inquiry-based reports instead of typical poster board formats.

- replace teacher-generated writing or photocopied sheets with student-generated print.

- incorporate the use of such skills as comparing and contrasting, recognizing cause and effect, and finding similarities and differences into daily work and long-term projects. For example, these Foldables can be used to compare and contrast student explanations and opinions with explanations and opinions currently accepted by experts in the field of health.

- continue to "immerse" students in previously learned vocabulary, concepts, information, generalizations, ideas, and theories, providing them with a strong foundation that they can build on with new observations, concepts, and knowledge.

- can be used by students or teachers to easily communicate data through graphs, tables, charts, models, and diagrams, including Venn diagrams.

- allow students to make their own journals for recording observations, research information, primary and secondary source data, surveys, and more.

- can be used as alternative assessment tools by teachers to evaluate student progress or by students to evaluate their own progress.

- integrate language arts, science, mathematics, and social studies into the study of health.

- provide a sense of student ownership or investment in the health curriculum.

Foldable Basics

What to Write and Where

Teach students to write general information such as titles, vocabulary words, concepts, questions, main ideas, and dates on the front tabs of their Foldables. This way students can easily recognize main ideas and important concepts. Foldables help students focus on and remember key points without being distracted by other print.

Ask students to write specific information such as supporting ideas, student thoughts, answers to questions, research information, class notes, observations, and definitions under the tabs.

As you teach, demonstrate different ways in which Foldables can be used. Soon you will find that students make their own Foldables and use them independently for study guides and projects.

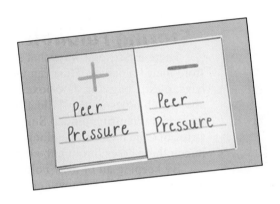

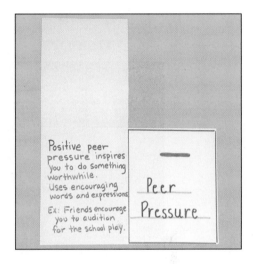

With or Without Tabs

Foldables with flaps, or tabs, create study guides that students can use to check what they know about the general information on the front of tabs. Use Foldables without tabs for assessment purposes or projects where information is presented for others to view quickly.

Venn diagram used as a study guide

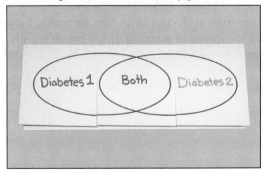

Venn diagram used for assessment

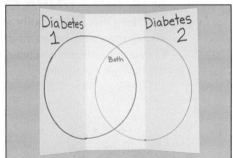

What to Do with Scissors and Glue

If it is d fficult for your students to keep glue and scissors at their desks, set up a small table in the classroom and provide several containers of glue, numerous pairs of scissors (sometimes tied to the table), containers of crayons and colored pencils, a stapler, clear tape, and anything else you think students might need to make their Foldables.

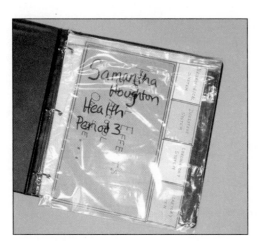

Storing Foldables

There are several ways that students can store their Foldables. They can use grocery bags, plastic bags, or shoe boxes. Students can also punch holes in their Foldables and place them in a three-ring binder. Suggest they place strips of 2-inch clear tape along one side and punch three holes through the taped edge.

By keeping all of their Foldables together and organized, students will create their own portfolio.

HINT: I found it more convenient to keep student portfolios in my classroom so that student work was always available when needed. Giant laundry-soap boxes make good storage containers for portfolios.

Use This Book As a Creative Resource

Have this book readily available for students to use as an idea reference for projects, discussions, debates, extra-credit work, cooperative learning group presentations, and so on. Encourage students to create their own versions of Foldables to help them learn the material the best way possible.

Basic Foldable Shapes

The following figures illustrate the basic folds that are referred to in this book.

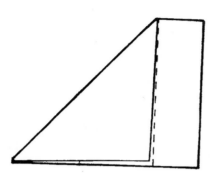

Taco Fold

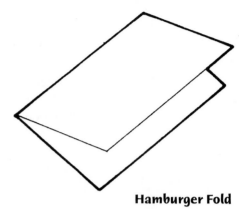

Hamburger Fold

Hot Dog Fold

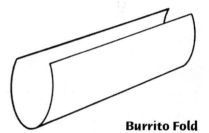

Burrito Fold

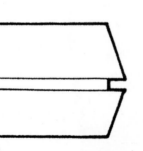

Shutter Fold

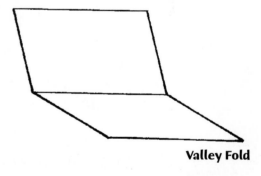

Valley Fold

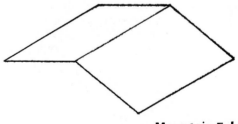

Mountain Fold

Half-Book

Fold a sheet of paper (8½″ × 11″) in half.

1. This book can be folded vertically like a hot dog.

2. It can also be folded horizontally like a hamburger.

Use this book for descriptive, expository, persuasive, or narrative writing, as well as for graphs, diagrams, or charts.

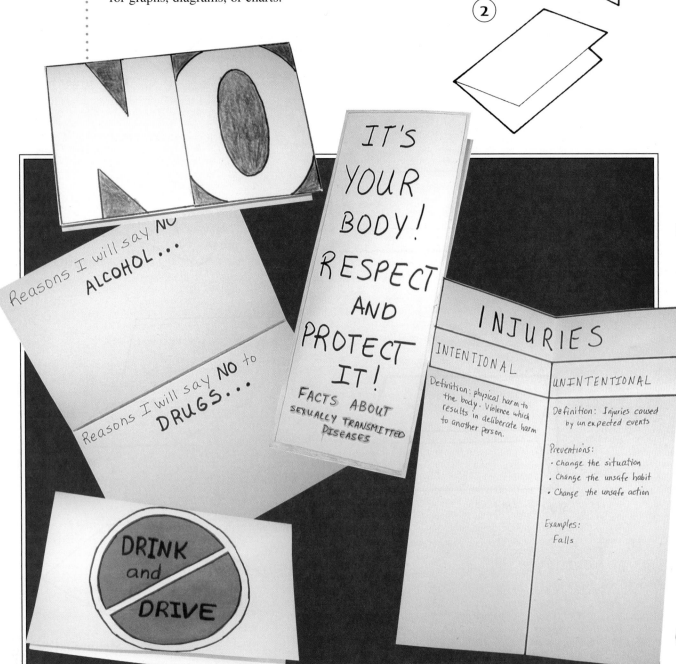

Folded Book

1. Make a half-book.

2. Fold it in half again like a hamburger. This makes a ready-made cover and two small pages for information on the inside.

Use photocopied work sheets, Internet printouts, and student-drawn diagrams or maps to make this book. One sheet of paper becomes two activities for two grades.

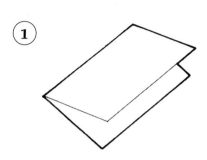

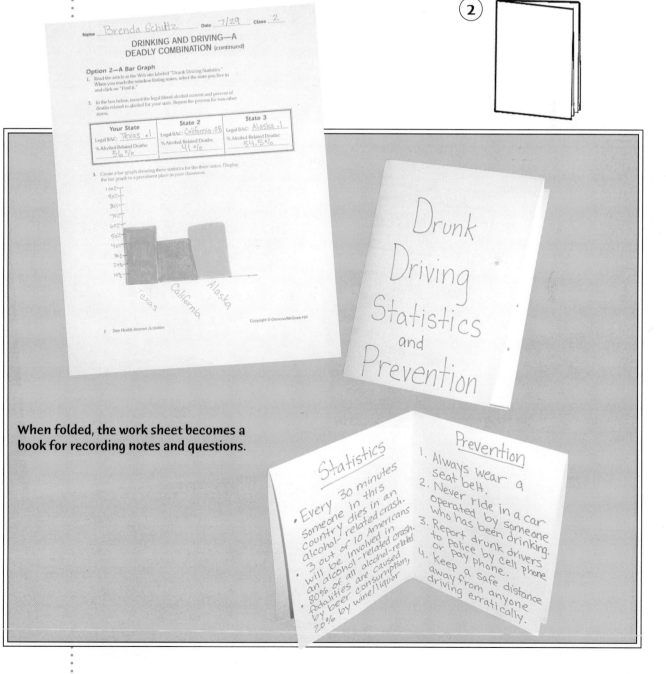

When folded, the work sheet becomes a book for recording notes and questions.

Three-Quarter Book

1. Take a two-tab book and raise the left-hand tab. (See page 11 for instructions on making a two-tab book.)

2. Cut the tab off at the top fold line.

3. A larger book of information can be made by gluing several three-quarter books side by side.

Sketch or glue a graphic on the left side, write one or more questions on the right tab, and record answers and information under the right tab.

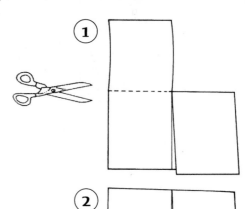

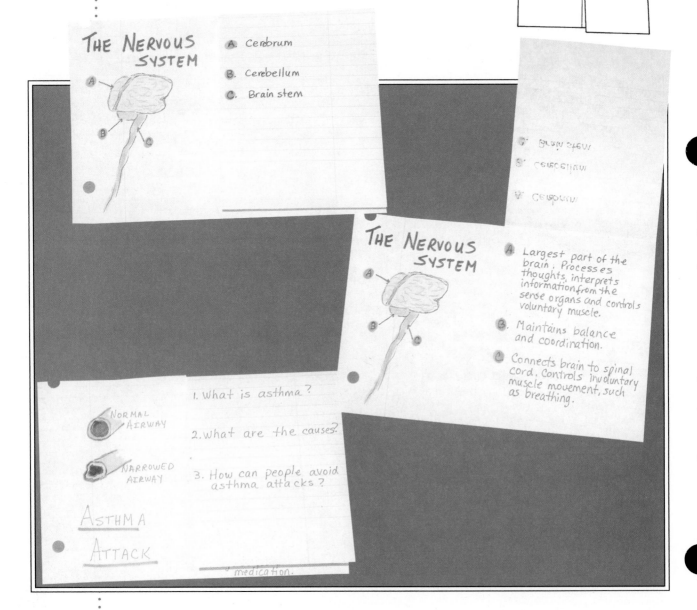

Bound Book

1. Take two sheets of paper (8½″ × 11″), and separately fold them like a hamburger. Place the papers on top of each other, leaving ¹⁄₁₆ inch between the mountaintops.

2. Mark both folds 1 inch from the outer edges.

3. On one of the folded sheets, cut from the top and bottom edge to the marked spot on both sides.

4. On the second folded sheet, start at one of the marked spots and cut the fold between the two marks.

5. Take the cut sheet from step 3 and fold it like a burrito. Place the burrito through the other sheet and then open the burrito. Fold the bound pages in half to form an eight-page book.

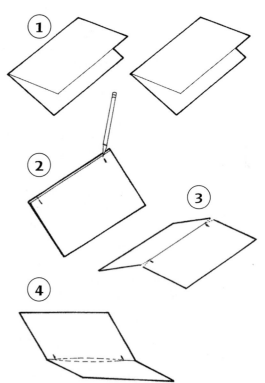

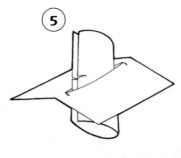

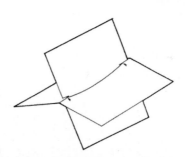

Picture Frame Book

1. Fold a sheet of paper (8½″ × 11″) in half like a hamburger.

2. Open the hamburger and gently roll one side of the hamburger toward the valley. Try not to crease the roll.

3. Cut a rectangle out of the middle of the rolled side of the paper, leaving a ½-inch border, forming a frame.

4. Fold another sheet of paper (8½″ × 11″) in half like a hamburger. Apply glue to the inside border of the picture frame and place the folded, uncut sheet of paper inside.

Use this book to feature a person, place, or thing. Inside the picture frame, glue a photograph, magazine picture, or computer-generated graph, or sketch a picture. This book has three inside pages for writing and recording notes.

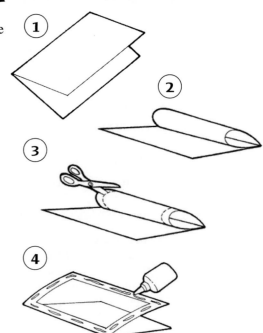

Two-Tab Book

1. Take a half book and cut up the valley of the inside fold toward the mountaintop. This cut forms two large tabs that can be used front and back for writing and illustrations.

Use this book with data occurring in twos. For example, use it for comparing and contrasting, determining cause and effect, and finding similarities and differences. The book can be expanded by making several of these folds and gluing them side by side.

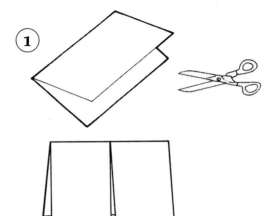

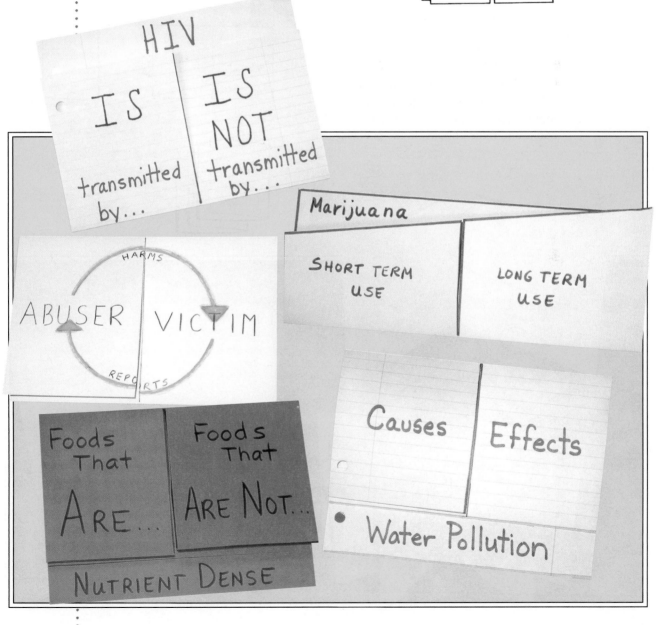

Pocket Book

1. Fold a sheet of paper (8½″ × 11″) in half like a hamburger.

2. Open the folded paper and fold one of the long sides up 2 inches to form a pocket. Refold along the hamburger fold so that the newly formed pockets are on the inside.

3. Glue the outer edges of the 2-inch fold with a small amount of glue.

4. **Optional:** Glue a cover around the pocket book.

   Variation: Make a multipaged booklet by gluing several pockets side by side. Glue a cover around the multipaged pocket book.

Use 3″ × 5″ index cards and quarter-sheets of notebook paper inside the pockets. Store student-made books, such as two-tab books and folded books, in the pockets.

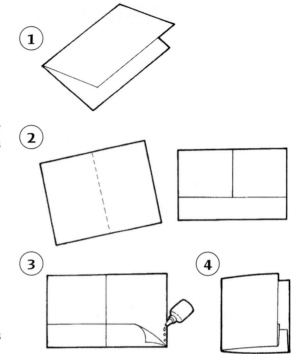

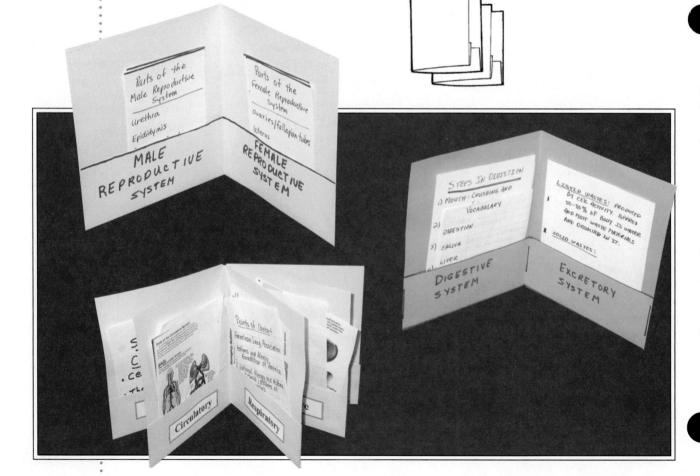

Matchbook

1. Fold a sheet of paper (8½″ × 11″) like a hamburger, but fold it so that one side is 1 inch longer than the other side.

2. Fold the 1-inch tab over the short side, forming an envelope-like fold.

3. Cut the front flap in half toward the mountaintop to create two flaps.

Use this book to report on one thing, such as one person, place, or thing, or for reporting on two things, such as the cause and effect of water pollution.

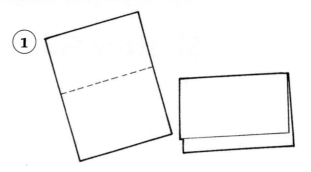

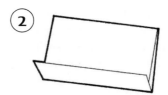

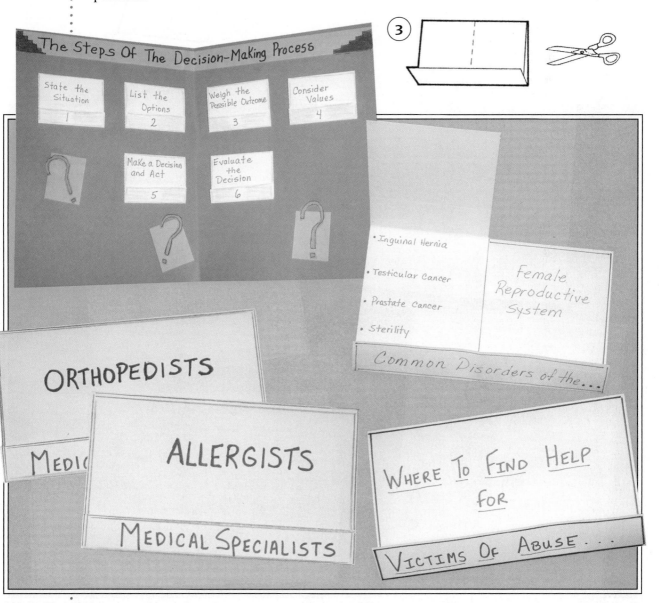

Shutter Fold

1. Begin as if you were going to make a hamburger, but instead of creasing the paper, pinch it to show the midpoint.

2. Fold the outer edges of the paper to meet at the pinch, or midpoint, forming a shutter fold.

Use this book for data occurring in twos. Or make this fold using 11″ × 17″ paper, and smaller books—such as the half-book, journal, and two-tab book—can be glued inside to create a large project full of student work.

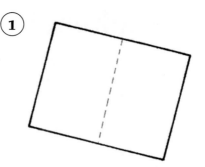

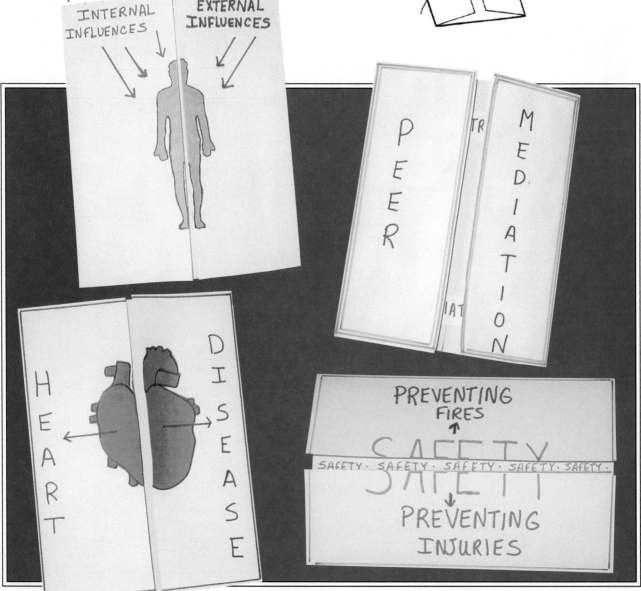

Forward-Backward Book

1. Stack three or more sheets of paper. On the top sheet trace a large circle.

2. With the papers still stacked, cut out the circles.

3. Staple the paper circles together along the left-hand side to create a book.

4. Label the cover and takes notes on the pages that open to the right.

5. Turn the book upside down and label the back. Takes notes on the pages that open to the right. Use one forward-backward book to compare and contrast two people, places, things, or events.

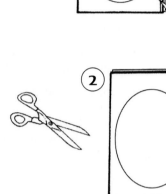

Front

Rheumatoid Arthritis

Back

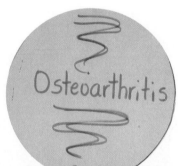

Osteoarthritis

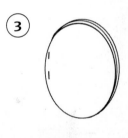

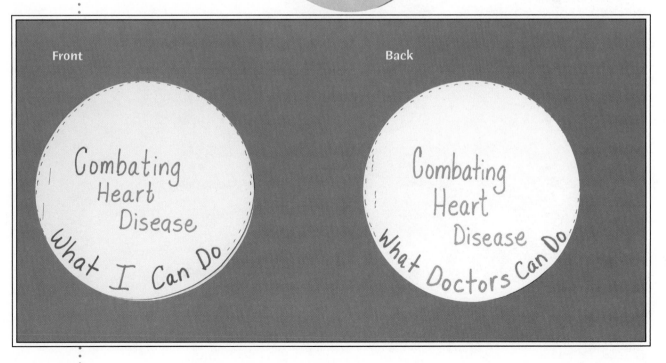

Front

Combating Heart Disease

What I Can Do

Back

Combating Heart Disease

What Doctors Can Do

Three-Tab Book

1. Fold a sheet of paper like a hot dog.

2. With the paper horizontal and the fold of the hot dog up, fold the right side toward the center, trying to cover one-half of the remaining paper.

NOTE: If you fold the right edge over first, the final graphic organizer will open and close like a book.

3. Fold the left side over the right side to make a book with three folds.

4. Open the folded book. Place your hands between the two thicknesses of paper and cut up the two valleys on one side only. This will form three tabs.

Use this book for data occurring in threes and for two-part Venn diagrams.

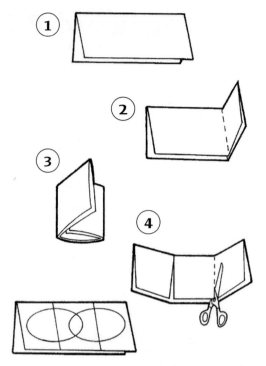

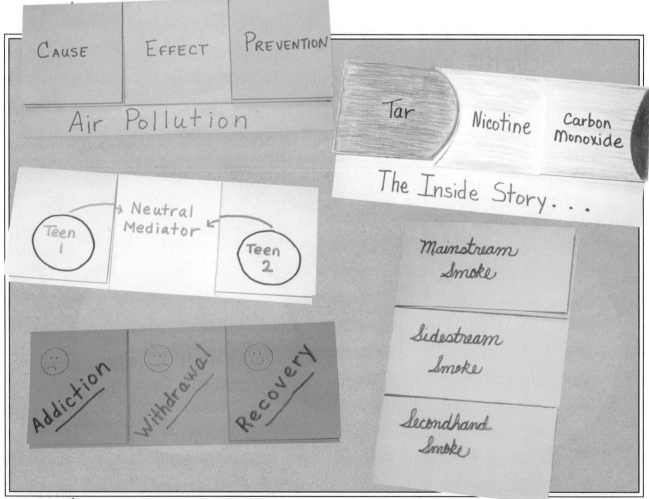

Three-Tab Book Variations

Variation A:
Draw overlapping circles on the three tabs to make a Venn Diagram

Variation B:
Cut each of the three tabs in half to make a six-tab book.

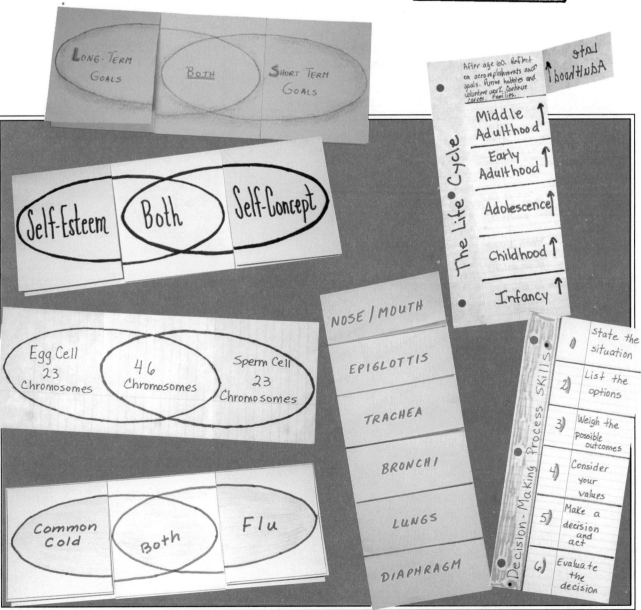
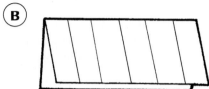
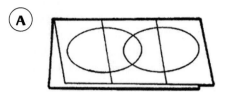

Pyramid Fold

1. Fold a sheet of paper (8½″ × 11″) into a taco. Cut off the excess rectangular tab formed by the fold. (The taco now forms a square when it is opened.)

2. Open the folded taco and refold it the opposite way, forming another taco and an X fold pattern.

3. Cut one of the folds to the center of the X, or the midpoint, and stop. This forms two triangular-shaped flaps.

4. Glue one of the flaps under the other, forming a pyramid.

5. Label front sections and write information, notes, thoughts, and questions inside the pyramid on the back of the appropriate tab.

Use to make mobiles and dioramas. Use with data occurring in threes.

① ②

③ ④

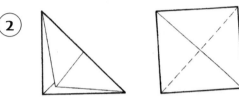

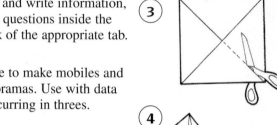

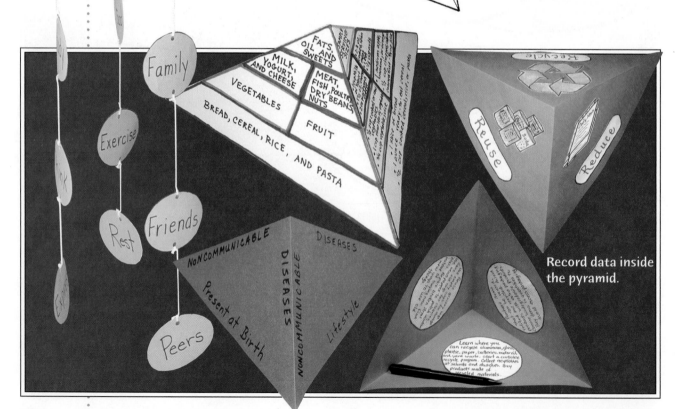

Record data inside the pyramid.

Trifold Book

1. Fold a sheet of paper (8½″ × 11″) into thirds.

2. Use this book as is, or cut into shapes. If the trifold is cut, leave plenty of fold on both sides of the designed shape so that the book will open and close in three sections.

Use this book to make charts with three columns or rows, large Venn diagrams, or reports on data occurring in threes, or use it to show the outside and inside of something and to write about it.

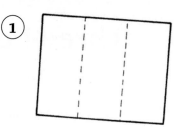

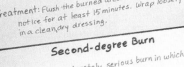

First-degree Burn

Definition: A burn in which only the outer layer of the skin is burned and turns red.

Treatment: Flush the burned area with cold water, not ice for at least 15 minutes. Wrap loosely in a clean, dry dressing.

Second-degree Burn

Definition: A moderately serious burn in which the burned area blisters.

Treatment: Flush the affected area with cold water, not ice, and elevate the burned area. Wrap in a clean, dry dressing. Do not pop blisters or peel loose skin.

Third-degree Burn

Definition: A very serious burn in which all layers of the skin are damaged.

Treatment: Requires immediate medical attention. Call 911 or an ambulance at once. Do not apply water or remove burned clothing. Keep the victim still and have her or him sip fluids.

The ABC's of Good Health
Aim for Fitness

Current fitness program:

necessary changes:

Build a Heathy Base

Current food choices:

necessary changes:

Choose Sensibly

Controlling: fat –

Sugar –

salt –

Advertising Technique

Good Times

Image Used

Teens having fun at a beach and drinking a brand name soft drink.

Hidden Message

I will have friends and good times if I use this product.

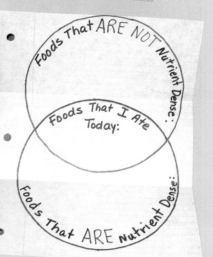

Foods That ARE NOT Nutrient Dense:

Foods That I Ate Today:

Foods That ARE Nutrient Dense:

Three-Pocket Book

1. Fold a horizontal sheet of paper (11″ × 17″) into thirds.

2. Fold the bottom edge up 2 inches and crease well. Glue the outer edges of the 2-inch tab to create three pockets.

3. Label each pocket. Use to hold notes taken on index cards or quarter-sheets of paper.

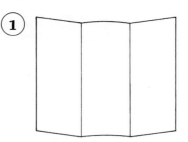

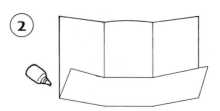

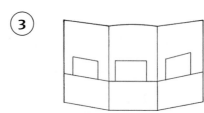

Four-Tab Book

1. Fold a sheet of paper (8½″ × 11″) in half like a hot dog.

2. Fold this long rectangle in half like a hamburger.

3. Fold both ends back to touch the mountain-top, folding it like an accordion.

4. On the side with two valleys and one mountaintop, make vertical cuts through one thickness of paper, forming four tabs.

Use this book for data occurring in fours. For example: skin, nails, hair, and teeth. You may leave the uncut side of the paper longer, to allow for an additional label.

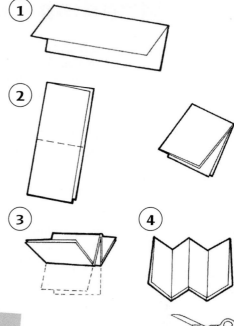

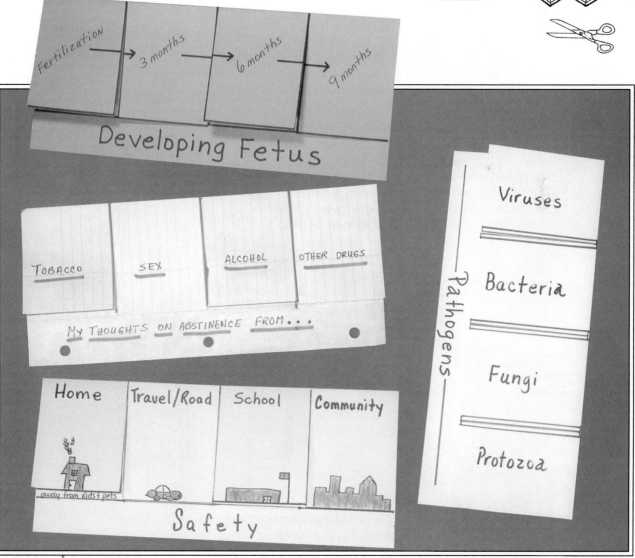

Standing Cube

1. Use two sheets of the same size paper. Fold each like a hamburger. However, fold one side ½ inch shorter than the other side. This will make a tab that extends out ½ inch on one side.

2. Fold the longer side over the shorter side of both sheets of paper, making tabs.

3. On one of the folded papers, place a small amount of glue along the the small folded tab, next to the valley but not in it.

4. Place the nonfolded edge of the second sheet of paper square into the valley and fold the glue-covered tab over this sheet of paper. Press flat until the glue holds. Repeat with the other side.

5. Allow the glue to dry completely before continuing. After the glue has dried, the cube can be collapsed flat to allow students to work at their desks. The cube can also be folded into fourths for easier storage or for moving it to a display area.

Use with data occurring in fours or make it into a project. Make a small display cube using 8½″ × 11″ paper. Use 11″ × 17″ paper to make large-cube projects that you can glue other books onto for display. Notebook paper, photocopied sheets, magazine pictures, and newspaper articles on current events can also be displayed on the large cube.

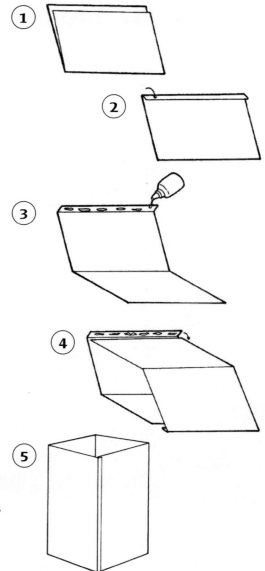

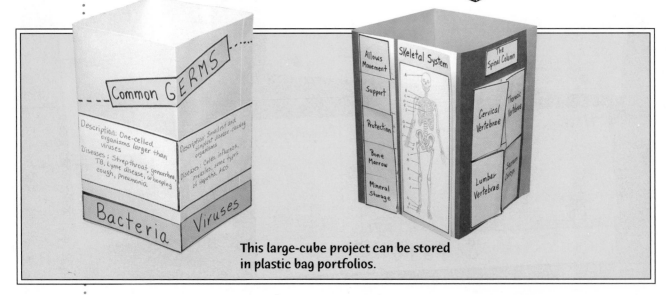

This large-cube project can be stored in plastic bag portfolios.

Four-Door Book

1. Make a shutter fold using 11″ × 17″ or 12″ × 18″ paper.

2. Fold the shutter fold in half like a hamburger. Crease well.

3. Open the project and cut along the two inside valley folds.

4. These cuts will form four doors on the inside of the project.

Use this fold for data occurring in fours. When folded in half like a hamburger, a finished four-door book can be glued inside a large (11″ × 17″) shutter fold as part of a larger project.

Envelope Fold

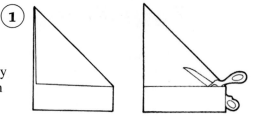

1. Fold a sheet of paper (8½″ × 11″) into a taco. Cut off the excess paper strip formed by the fold. (The taco now forms a square when it is opened.)

2. Open the folded taco and refold it the opposite way, forming another taco and an X fold pattern.

3. Open the taco fold and fold the corners toward the center point of the X, forming a small square.

4. Trace this square on another sheet of paper. Cut and glue it to the inside of the envelope. Pictures can be placed under or on top of the tabs.

Use this book for data occurring in fours. For example: infancy, childhood, adolescence, and adulthood. The book can also be used to teach fractional parts.

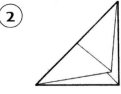

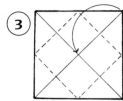

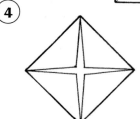

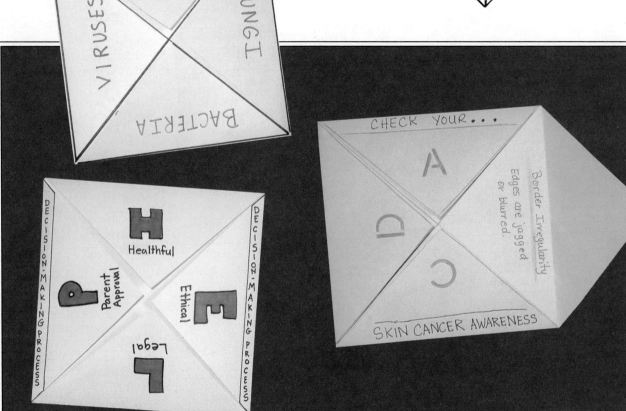

Layered-Look Book

1. Stack two sheets of paper (8½″ × 11″) so that the back sheet is 1 inch higher than the front sheet.

2. Bring the bottom of both sheets upward and align the edges so that all of the layers, or tabs, are the same distance apart.

3. When all tabs are an equal distance apart, fold the papers and crease well.

4. Open the papers and glue them together along the valley (inner center fold), or staple them along the mountain.

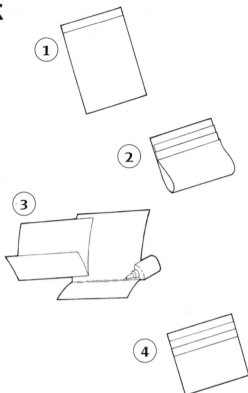

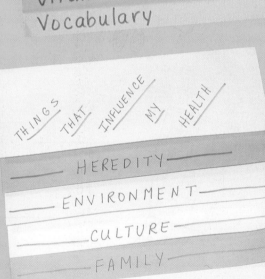

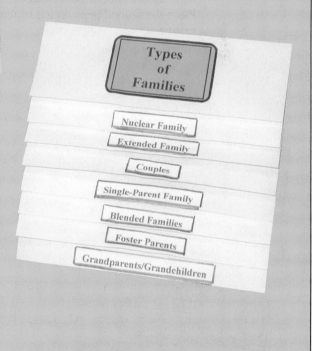

Six Major Nutrients For Health

Carbohydrates
Proteins
Fats
Minerals
Water
Vitamins
Vocabulary

THINGS THAT INFLUENCE MY HEALTH

HEREDITY
ENVIRONMENT
CULTURE
FAMILY
MEDIA

Types of Families

Nuclear Family
Extended Family
Couples
Single-Parent Family
Blended Families
Foster Parents
Grandparents/Grandchildren

When using more than two sheets of paper, make the tabs smaller than an inch.

Top-Tab Book

1. Fold a sheet of paper (8½″ × 11″) in half like a hamburger. Cut the center fold, forming two half-sheets.

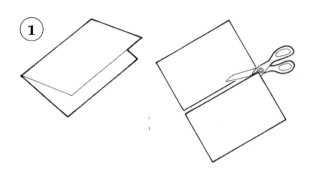

2. Fold one of the half-sheets four times. Begin by folding in half like a hamburger, then again like a hamburger, yet again like a hamburger, and finally again like a hamburger. This folding forms a pattern of four rows and four columns, or 16 small squares.

3. Fold two sheets of paper (8½″ × 11″) in half like a hamburger. Cut the center folds, forming four half-sheets.

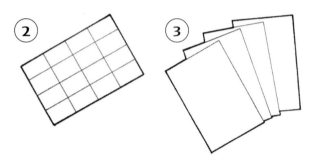

4. Hold the pattern vertically and place on a half-sheet of paper under the pattern. Cut the bottom right-hand square out of both sheets. Set this first page aside.

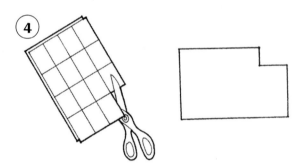

5. Take a second half-sheet of paper and place it under the pattern. Cut the first and second bottom right-hand squares out of both sheets. Place the second page on top of the first page.

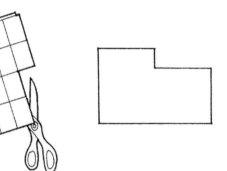

6. Take a third half-sheet of paper and place it under the pattern. Cut the first, second, and third bottom right-hand squares out of both sheets. Place this third page on top of the second page.

7. Place the fourth uncut half-sheet of paper behind the three cut-out sheets, leaving four aligned tabs across the top of the book. Staple several times on the left side. You can also place glue along the left paper edges and stack them together. The glued spine is very strong.

8. Cut a final half-sheet of paper with no tabs and staple along the left side to form a cover.

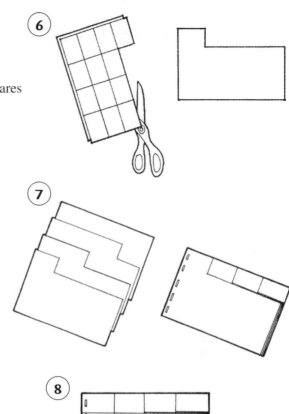

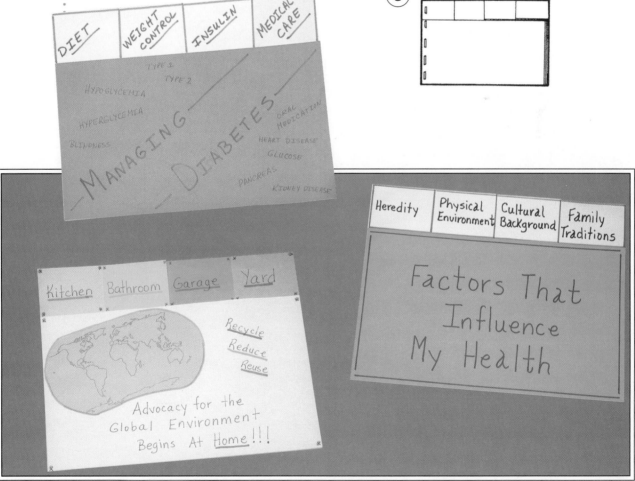

Folding a Circle into Tenths

1. Fold a paper circle in half.

2. Fold the half-circle so that one-third is exposed and two-thirds are covered.

3. Fold the one-third (single thickness) backward to form a fold line.

4. Fold the two-thirds section in half.

5. The half-circle will be divided into fifths. When opened, the circle will be divided into tenths.

NOTE: Paper squares and rectangles are folded into tenths the same way. Fold them so that one-third is exposed and two-thirds are covered. Continue with steps 3 and 4.

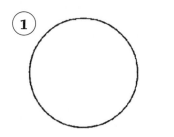

2/3

1/3

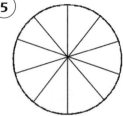

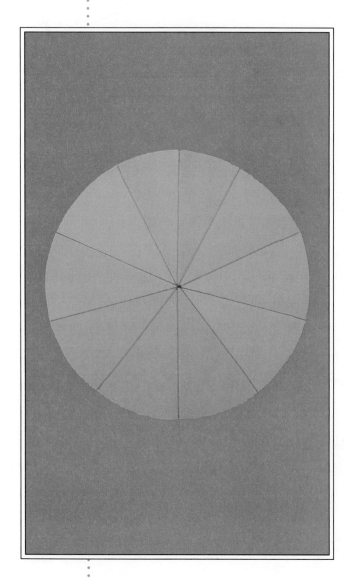

Circle Graph

1. Cut out two circles using a pattern.

2. Fold each of the circles in half on each axis, forming fourths. Cut along one of the fold lines (the radius) to the middle of each circle. Flatten the circles.

3. Slip the two circles together along the cuts until they overlap completely.

4. Spin one of the circles while holding the other stationary. Estimate how much of each of the two (or you can add more) circles should be exposed to illustrate given percentages or fractional parts of data. Add circles to represent more than two percentages.

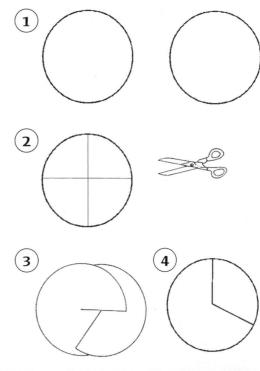

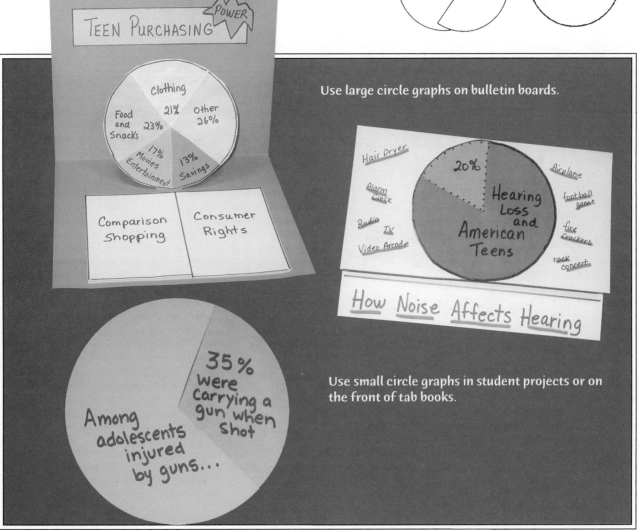

Use large circle graphs on bulletin boards.

Use small circle graphs in student projects or on the front of tab books.

Folding into Fifths

1. Fold a sheet of paper in half like a hot dog or hamburger for a five-tab book, or leave open for a folded table or chart.

2. Fold the paper so that one-third is exposed and two-thirds are covered.

3. Fold the two-thirds section in half.

4. Fold the one-third section (single thickness) backward to form a fold line. The paper will be divided into fifths when opened.

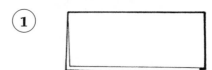

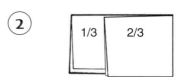

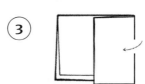

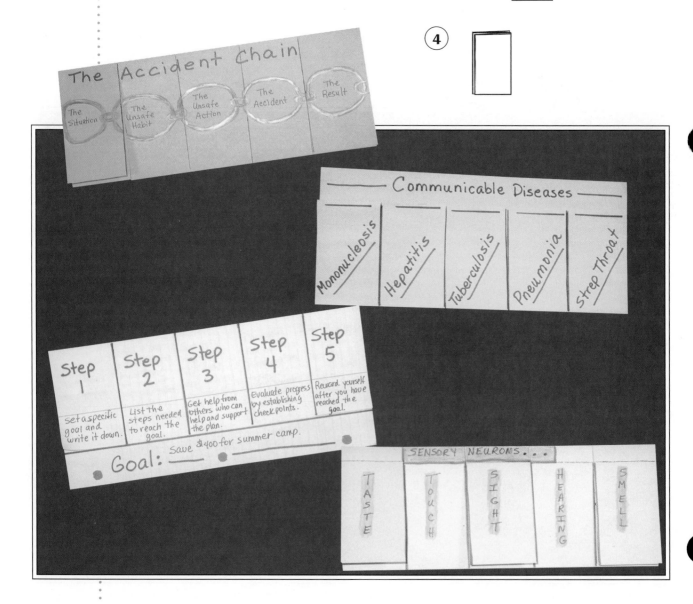

Folded Table or Chart

1. Fold the number of vertical columns needed to make the table or chart.

2. Fold the horizontal rows needed to make the table or chart.

3. Label the rows and columns.

Remember: Tables are organized along vertical and horizontal axes, while charts are organized along one axis, either horizontal or vertical.

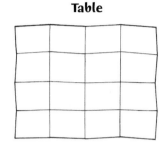

Table

Chart

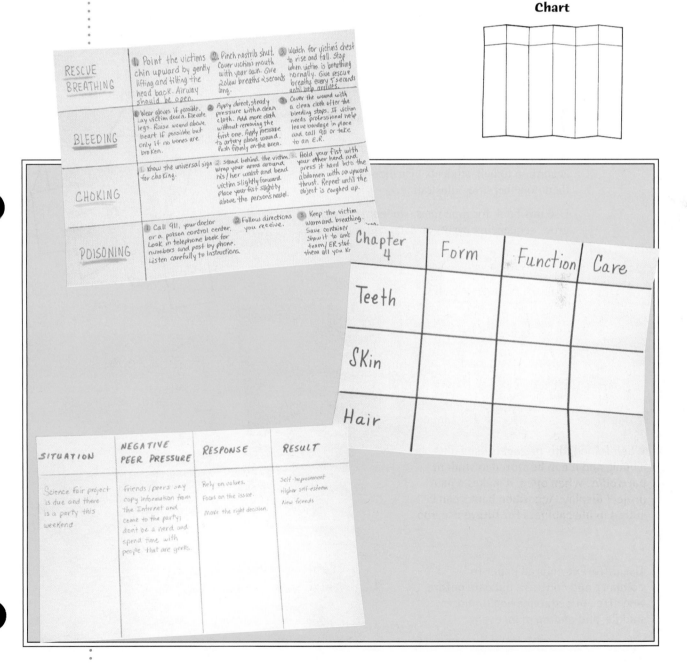

Accordion Book

NOTE: Steps 1 and 2 should be done only if paper is too large to begin with.

1. Fold the selected paper into hamburgers.

2. Cut the paper in half along the fold lines.

3. Fold each section of paper into a hamburger. However, fold one side ½ inch shorter than the other side. This will form a tab that is ½ inch long.

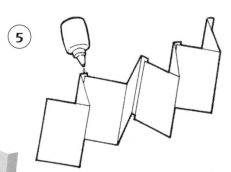

4. Fold this tab forward over the shorter side, and then fold it back away from the shorter piece of paper (in other words, fold it the opposite way).

5. Glue together to form an accordion by gluing a straight edge of one section into the valley of another section. Always place the extra tab at the back of the book so you can add more pages later.

NOTE: Stand the sections on end to form an accordion to help students visualize how to glue them together. (See illustration.)

Use this book for time lines, student projects that grow, sequencing events or data, and biographies.

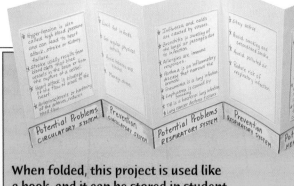

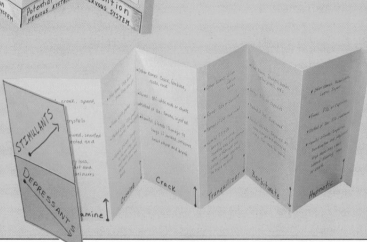

When folded, this project is used like a book, and it can be stored in student portfolios. When open, it makes a nice project display. Accordion books can be stored in file cabinets for future use, too.

Use different-colored paper to compare and contrast, indicate before and after, or sequence beginning, middle, and ending of an event.

Pop-Up Book

1. Fold a sheet of paper (8½″ × 11″) in half like a hamburger.

2. Beginning at the fold, or mountaintop, cut one or more tabs.

3. Fold the tabs back and forth several times until there is a good fold line formed.

4. Partially open the hamburger fold and push the tabs through to the inside.

5. **Optionals.** With one small dot of glue, glue figures for the pop-up book to the front of each tab. Allow the glue to dry before going on to the next step.

6. Make a cover for the book by folding another sheet of paper in half like a hamburger. Place glue around the outside edges of the pop-up book and firmly press inside the hamburger cover.

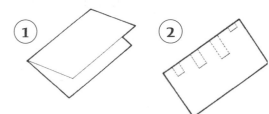
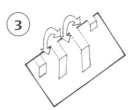
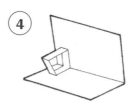
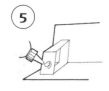
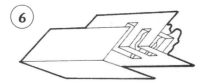

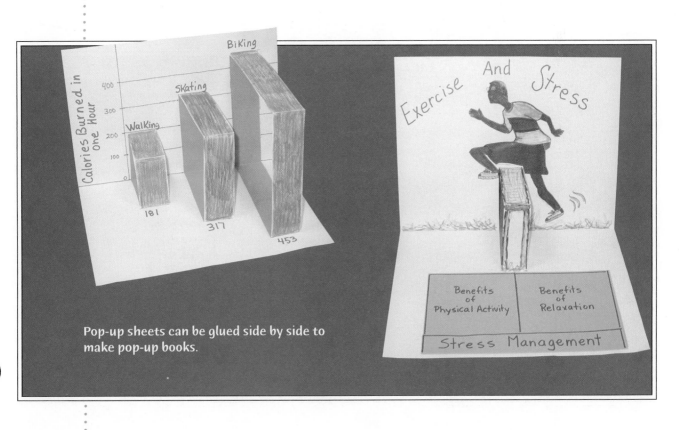

Pop-up sheets can be glued side by side to make pop-up books.

Four-Door Diorama

1. Make a four-door book out of a shutter fold.

2. Fold the two inside corners back to the outer edges (mountains) of the shutter fold. This will result in two tacos that will make the four-door book look like it has a shirt collar. Do the same thing to the bottom of the four-door book. When finished, four small triangles (tacos) have been made.

3. Form a 90-degree angle and overlap the folded triangles to make a display case that doesn't use staples or glue. (It can be collapsed for storage.) Or, as illustrated, cut off all four triangles, or tacos. Staple or glue the sides.

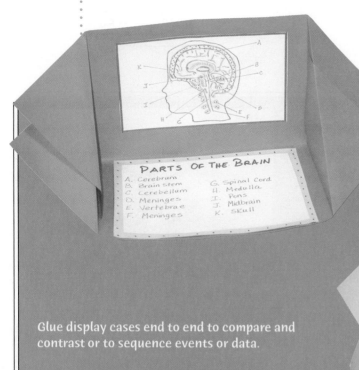

PARTS OF THE BRAIN

A. Cerebrum
B. Brain stem
C. Cerebellum
D. Meninges
E. Vertebrae
F. Meninges
G. Spinal Cord
H. Medulla
I. Pons
J. Midbrain
K. Skull

Glue display cases end to end to compare and contrast or to sequence events or data.

Use 11″ × 17″ paper to make a large display case.

Use poster board to make giant display cases.

Food Labels Have a Lot to Say:
• Serving Size
• Calories
• Nutrients
• Percent Daily Value

Concept-Map Book

1. Fold a sheet of paper along the long or short axis, leaving a 2-inch tab uncovered along the top.

2. Fold the other way in half or in thirds.

3. Unfold and cut along the two or three inside fold lines.

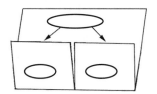

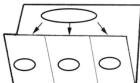

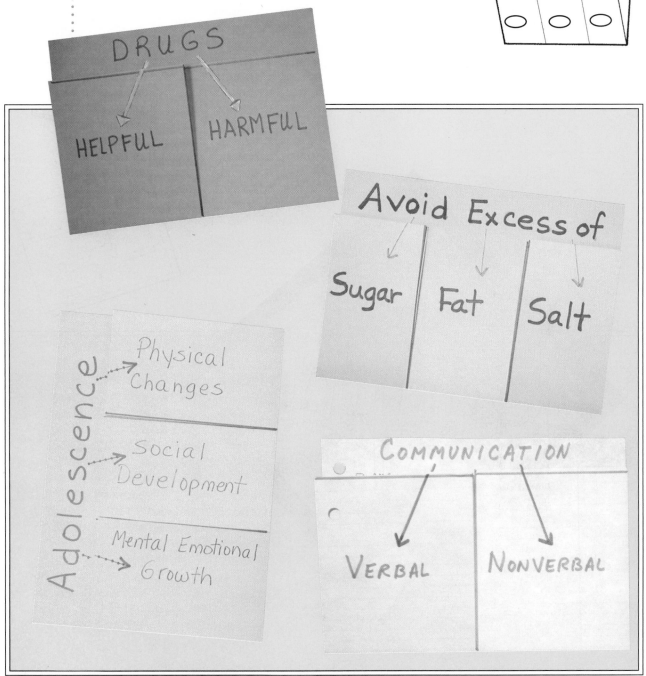

Project Board with Tabs

1. Draw a large illustration or a series of small illustrations or write on the front of one of the pieces of selected-size paper.

2. Pinch and slightly fold the paper at the point where a tab is desired on the illustrated project board. Cut into the paper on the fold. Cut straight in, then cut up to form an L. When the paper is unfolded, it will form a tab with an illustration on the front.

3. After all tabs have been cut, glue this front sheet onto a second piece of paper. Place glue around all four edges and in the middle, away from tabs.

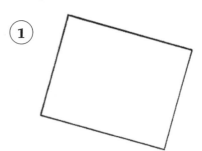

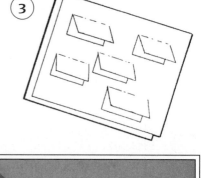

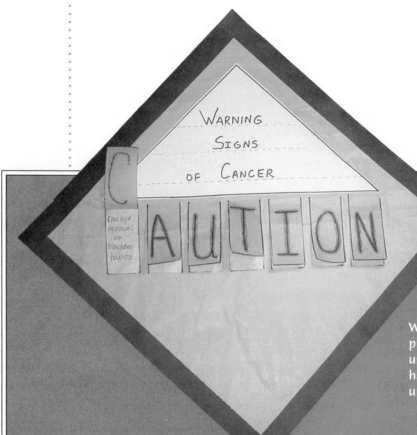

Write or draw under the tabs. If the project is made as a bulletin board using butcher paper, quarter- and half-sheets of paper can be glued under the tabs.

Billboard Project

1. Fold all pieces of the same size of paper in half like hamburgers.

2. Place a line of glue at the top and bottom of one side of each folded billboard section and glue them edge to edge on a background paper or project board. If glued correctly, all doors will open from right to left.

3. Pictures, dates, or words go on the front of each billboard section. When opened, writing or drawings can be seen on the inside of each section. The base, or the part glued to the background, is perfect for more in-depth information or definitions.

Use for time lines or sequencing data, such as the stages of pregnancy or the path of the digestive system.

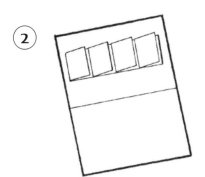

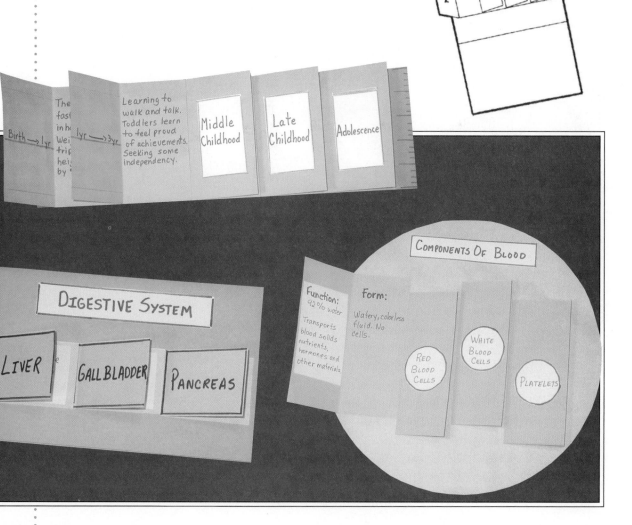

Vocabulary Book

1. Fold a sheet of notebook paper in half like a hot dog.

2. On one side, cut every third line. This results in ten tabs on wide-ruled notebook paper and twelve tabs on college-ruled paper.

3. Label the tabs.

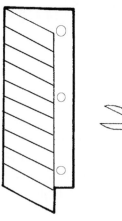

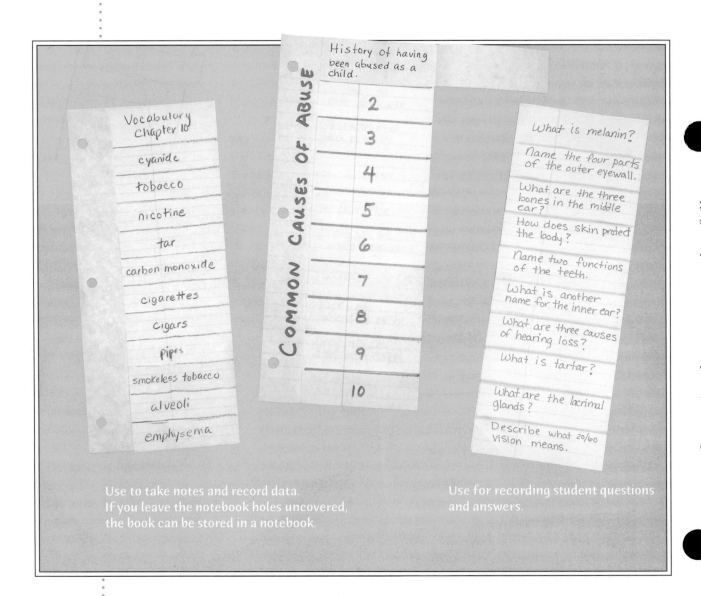

Vocabulary
Chapter 10

cyanide

tobacco

nicotine

tar

carbon monoxide

cigarettes

cigars

pipes

smokeless tobacco

alveoli

emphysema

COMMON CAUSES OF ABUSE

History of having been abused as a child.

2

3

4

5

6

7

8

9

10

What is melanin?

Name the four parts of the outer eyewall.

What are the three bones in the middle ear?

How does skin protect the body?

Name two functions of the teeth.

What is another name for the inner ear?

What are three causes of hearing loss?

What is tartar?

What are the lacrimal glands?

Describe what 20/60 vision means.

Use to take notes and record data.
If you leave the notebook holes uncovered,
the book can be stored in a notebook.

Use for recording student questions
and answers.

Sentence Strips

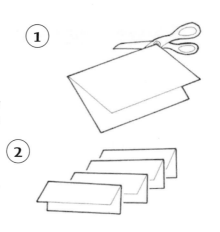

1. Take two sheets of paper (8½″ × 11″) and fold into hamburgers. Cut along the fold lines, making four half-sheets. (Use as many half-sheets as necessary for additional pages to your book.)

2. Fold each sheet in half like a hot dog.

3. Place the folds side by side, and staple them together on the left side.

4. One inch from the stapled edge, cut the front page of each folded section up to the mountaintop. These cuts form flaps that can be raised and lowered.

To make a half-cover, use a sheet of construction paper 1 inch longer than the book. Glue the back of the last sheet to the construction paper strip, leaving 1 inch on the left side to fold over and cover the original staples. Staple this half-cover in place.

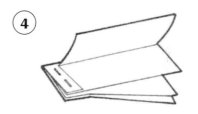

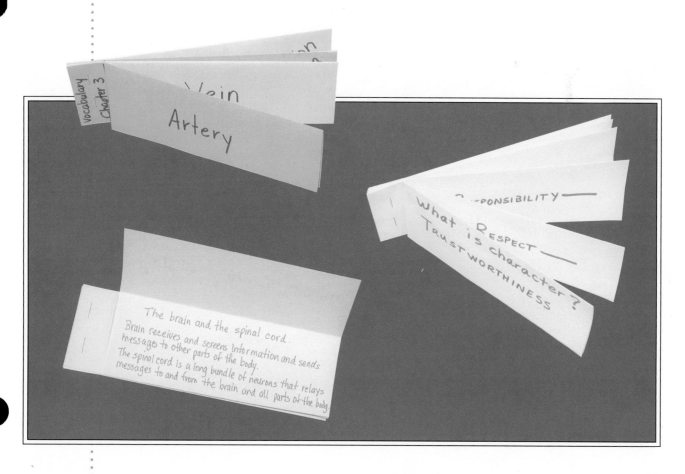

Sentence-Strip Holder

1. Fold a sheet of paper (8½″ × 11″) in half like a hamburger.

2. Open the hamburger and fold the two outer edges toward the valley. This forms a shutter fold.

3. Fold one of the inside edges of the shutter back to the outside fold. This fold forms a floppy L.

4. Glue the floppy L tab down to the base so that it forms a strong, straight L tab.

5. Glue the other shutter side to the front of this L tab. This forms a tent that is the backboard for the flashcards or student work to be displayed. Fold the edge of the L tab up one-quarter to one-half to form a lip that will keep the student work from slipping off the holder.

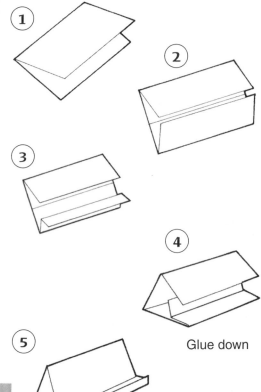

Glue down

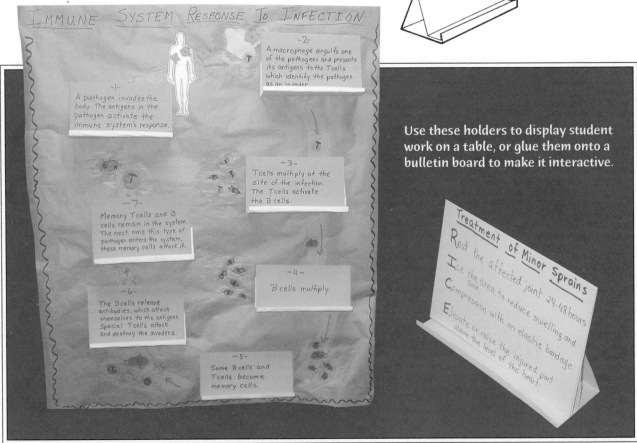

Use these holders to display student work on a table, or glue them onto a bulletin board to make it interactive.

FOLDABLES™

Chapter Activities for

Teen Health

Course 1

Course 2

Course 3

Your Health and Wellness

CHAPTER SUMMARY

Good health depends on balance among the three parts of the health triangle: physical health, mental/emotional health, and social health. Ten skills are important to maintaining good health: accessing information, practicing healthful behaviors, stress management, analyzing influences, communication skills, conflict resolution, refusal skills, decision making, goal setting, and advocacy. The decision-making process and good character lead to healthier choices. Achieving short- and long-term goals leads to positive changes.

CHAPTER PREVIEW

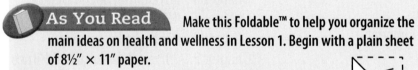

As You Read Make this Foldable™ to help you organize the main ideas on health and wellness in Lesson 1. Begin with a plain sheet of 8½″ × 11″ paper.

1 Line up one of the short edges of a sheet of paper with one of the long edges to form a triangle. Fold and cut off the leftover rectangle.

2 Fold the triangle in half, then unfold. The folds will form an *X* dividing the paper into four equal sections.

3 Cut along one fold line, and stop at the middle. This forms two triangular flaps. Draw an *X* on one tab, and label the other three as shown.

4 Fold the *X* flap under the other flap, and glue together to make a three-sided pyramid.

Write the main ideas about the three parts of health on the back of the appropriate side of the pyramid.

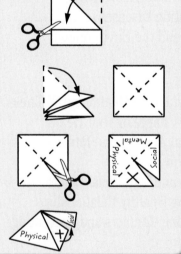

CHAPTER REVIEW

Foldables Follow-Up Activity

Divide the class into small groups. Ask them to discuss difficulties they or someone they know has had in reaching a goal in one of the three areas of health written on their Foldable. How were the difficulties overcome? What have they learned in class that might have helped resolve the difficulty?

Alternative Activities for Chapter 1

IDENTIFYING

Have students complete the first three steps of the Foldable instructions. Instead of the labels given, have students list the six decision-making steps from page 17 of the Student Edition on one side of a pyramid Foldable. Ask them to write the first step at the bottom and the last at the top, and encourage them to think of the early steps as a foundation for the other steps. Then have them write a health-related problem on another side of the pyramid. On the remaining side, have students identify what could be done at each step to make a decision or solve the problem. Have students complete Step 4 of the Foldable instructions to complete their pyramids.

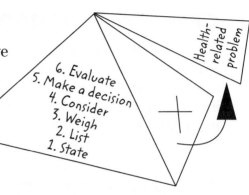

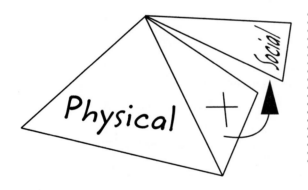

ANALYZING

Have students complete the Foldable instructions. Ask them to choose one of the ten health skills. Have students write ways in which that skill might affect a person in terms of each of the three categories on the back of the appropriate side of the pyramid.

Student Study Tip

Encourage students to become familiar with their textbooks so they can find things more easily. Point out the different features, such as Reading Check. Ask them to explain the purposes of the Glossary, Index, and Table of Contents. Where would they be most likely to find the definition of a word? Ask them to explain the difference between a chapter and a lesson. Do lessons have review questions? Do chapters? On what page does the assessment for Chapter 1 begin?

Course 1

FOLDABLES

Mental and Emotional Wellness

CHAPTER SUMMARY

Self-concept is what a person thinks of himself or herself. Developing a positive self-concept helps a person appreciate and improve his or her good points. Expressing emotions in healthy ways encourages good mental and emotional health. Stress may be positive or negative. Too much stress can damage health, but effective ways of managing stress can be learned.

CHAPTER PREVIEW

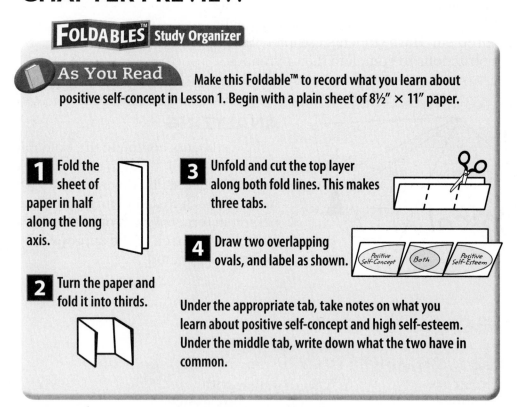

FOLDABLES™ Study Organizer

As You Read Make this Foldable™ to record what you learn about positive self-concept in Lesson 1. Begin with a plain sheet of 8½″ × 11″ paper.

1 Fold the sheet of paper in half along the long axis.

2 Turn the paper and fold it into thirds.

3 Unfold and cut the top layer along both fold lines. This makes three tabs.

4 Draw two overlapping ovals, and label as shown.

Positive Self-Concept *Both* *Positive Self-Esteem*

Under the appropriate tab, take notes on what you learn about positive self-concept and high self-esteem. Under the middle tab, write down what the two have in common.

CHAPTER REVIEW

Foldables Follow-Up Activity

Have students think of a fictional character in a favorite story or TV show who does not seem to have a positive self-concept. Ask them to use their Foldable as a reference and, based on what they've learned in class, write a letter to that character suggesting ways he or she could develop a more positive self-concept.

Alternative Activities for Chapter 2

COMPARING

Have students create a new three-tab Foldable. Under the left tab, have them list the four healthy ways to express strong emotions. Under the right tab, have them list the ways to manage stress. Under the middle tab, have them list ways that expressing strong emotions and managing stress are alike. Discuss with them how stress and emotions are often related. Stress can trigger strong emotions and make problems seem worse.

IDENTIFYING

Write the following on the board: "Mei has just found out that she did poorly on an English test because she misread the instructions. Now she is about to take a math test." Ask students to create a three-tab Foldable. Under one tab, have them list some unhealthy responses Mei might have to her situation. Under another tab, have them list healthy responses she could choose instead. Under the third tab, have them list people Mei can turn to for help or support.

Student Study Tip

Ask students to think about the work their parents or caregivers do. What tools do they use? A carpenter, for example, might use a power drill; an executive might need a laptop computer or calculator; a cook might require measuring cups. These are the "tools of their trade." What would happen if they showed up at work without these tools? Would they be paid that day for work they couldn't do? Ask the class to observe students who do well in school. Their books, notebooks, and pencils are the tools of their trade. Do they leave them at home or do they come to class prepared to do the job?

Course 1

FOLDABLES

Healthy Relationships

CHAPTER SUMMARY

There are many kinds of families, but healthy families all share the same goal: to seek the well-being of their members. In addition to family relationships, people have relationships with friends and peers. Friends become especially important during the teen years. Friends and peers help people meet many social needs. Good communication helps build healthy relationships. Communication can involve words, facial expressions, gestures, and posture. Along with compromise and peer remediation, it can help resolve conflicts.

CHAPTER PREVIEW

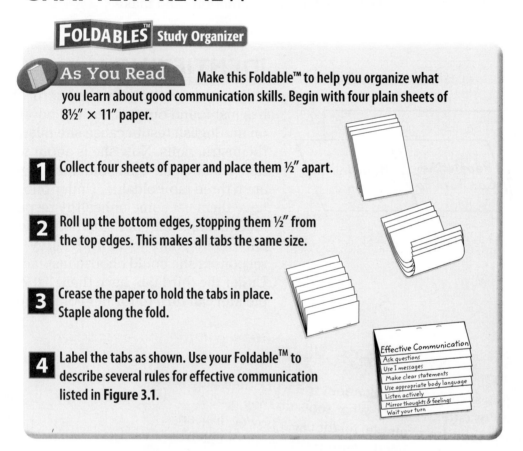

FOLDABLES™ Study Organizer

As You Read Make this Foldable™ to help you organize what you learn about good communication skills. Begin with four plain sheets of 8½" × 11" paper.

1 Collect four sheets of paper and place them ½" apart.

2 Roll up the bottom edges, stopping them ½" from the top edges. This makes all tabs the same size.

3 Crease the paper to hold the tabs in place. Staple along the fold.

4 Label the tabs as shown. Use your Foldable™ to describe several rules for effective communication listed in **Figure 3.1**.

Effective Communication
Ask questions
Use I messages
Make clear statements
Use appropriate body language
Listen actively
Mirror thoughts & feelings
Wait your turn

CHAPTER REVIEW

Foldables Follow-Up Activity

Explain to students the concept of a family tree. Ask them to draw and label a family tree for their own families, going back to grandparents and including aunts, uncles, and cousins. Have them refer to their Foldables to list ways in which family members on their family tree communicate with one another. Have them put a star by those people they communicate with often. Have them put two stars by those who support their positive self-concept in some way.

Alternative Activities for Chapter 3

DRAWING CONCLUSIONS

Have students complete the first three steps of the Foldable instructions. Have them label the Foldable with the ways in which conflicts develop. Then have students describe a way to prevent each type of conflict.

How Conflicts Develop
- Differing Expectations
- Differing Values
- Hurt Feelings
- Changing Roles
- Jealousy
- Possessions
- Struggle for Power

Effective Communication
- Ask questions
- Use I messages
- Make clear statements
- Use appropriate body language
- Listen actively
- Mirror thoughts & feelings
- Wait your turn

IDENTIFYING

Have students complete the first three steps of the Foldable instructions. Have them label the Foldable with the skills for being a good speaker and a good listener. For each skill, have them note whether the skill involves words, facial expressions, gestures, or posture. Some skills may involve more than one type of communication.

Student Study Tip

Suggest that students visit the school library or media center to become more familiar with it. The catalogs for most libraries are now on computer, and the systems may be frequently updated. Students should know how to use the latest system and should ask the librarian if they have any questions. Suggest that they make a map of the library so they can quickly find the encyclopedias, dictionaries, nonfiction books, newspapers, maps, and other important resources. Remind them to check library hours. Is the library open to students early? Does it stay open late?

Course 1

FOLDABLES

Nutrition

CHAPTER SUMMARY

There are six basic nutrients that the body needs: carbohydrates, proteins, fats, vitamins, minerals, and water. MyPyramid is a tool that can be used to plan healthful food choices. A healthy eating plan includes a variety of foods. Physical activity and fitness improve physical, mental/emotional, and social health. Exercise should begin with a warm-up and end with a cool-down.

CHAPTER PREVIEW

FOLDABLES™ Study Organizer

As You Read Make this Foldable™ to help you organize the material in Lesson 1 on nutrients. Begin with a plain sheet of 8½" × 11" paper, or one sheet of notebook paper.

1 Fold a sheet of paper along the long axis, leaving a ½" tab along the side.

2 Turn the paper, and fold into thirds.

3 Cut the top layer along both folds. Then cut each tab in half to make six tabs.

4 Turn the paper vertically, and label the tabs as shown. Under the appropriate tab, write down major concepts, definitions, and food sources of each type of nutrient.

Carbohydrates
Proteins
Fats
Vitamins
Minerals
Water

CHAPTER REVIEW

Foldables Follow-Up Activity

Have students use the information on their Foldable to create a poster showing the nutrients in foods and why those nutrients are important. Ask that they indicate on their poster in which of the different food groups the nutrients occur.

Alternative Activities for Chapter 4

SHARING INFORMATION

Have students follow the first three steps of the Foldable instructions twice, to make two Foldables. On one Foldable, have them write the names of foods that they like. Under the appropriate tab, they should write down the way the food is prepared that they find appealing. On the other Foldable, have them write the names of foods they have not yet learned to like. Then ask students to trade their Foldable with a classmate and compare their likes and dislikes.

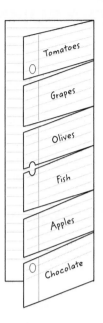

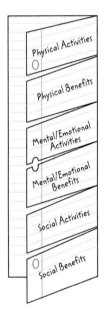

RESEARCHING

Have students follow the first three steps of the Foldable instructions. Have students label the tabs "Physical Activities," "Physical Benefits," "Mental/ Emotional Activities," "Mental/Emotional Benefits," "Social Activities," and "Social Benefits." Under each Activities tab, have students identify an activity that benefits that factor of health. Under each Benefits tab, have students identify the health benefits of that activity.

Student Study Tip

Suggest to students that they keep a homework and test log. The log should have space for noting the class; the date the assignment is made, the date it's due; important information about the assignment, such as page numbers; and a list of any materials needed. At the end of the day, students can pull out the log and know exactly what's expected of them and when they must turn in assignments. The handiest kind of log is a medium-sized notebook dedicated to this one purpose and clearly marked with the student's name.

Course 1

FOLDABLES

Physical Activity

CHAPTER SUMMARY

Physical activity is any movement that causes your body to use energy. Being physically fit has physical, mental/emotional, and social benefits. Physical activity can make your body strong. Before starting a physical fitness program, it's important to establish a personal fitness plan. The plan starts with a fitness goal. The F.I.T.T. principle is a method for safely increasing aspects of your workout without injuring yourself. Physical activity can be fun, but it should also be safe. One way to be safe is to always use the proper sports gear. All physical activities carry the risk of injury. The word *PRICE* can help you remember how to treat injuries.

CHAPTER PREVIEW

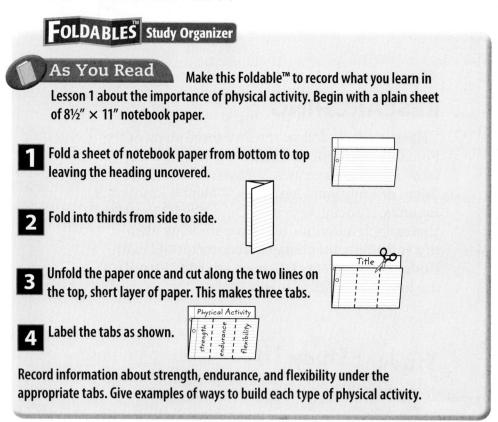

FOLDABLES™ Study Organizer

As You Read Make this Foldable™ to record what you learn in Lesson 1 about the importance of physical activity. Begin with a plain sheet of 8½″ × 11″ notebook paper.

1 Fold a sheet of notebook paper from bottom to top leaving the heading uncovered.

2 Fold into thirds from side to side.

3 Unfold the paper once and cut along the two lines on the top, short layer of paper. This makes three tabs.

4 Label the tabs as shown.

Record information about strength, endurance, and flexibility under the appropriate tabs. Give examples of ways to build each type of physical activity.

CHAPTER REVIEW

Foldables Follow-Up Activity

After students have completed their Foldable and have listed examples of physical benefits, divide the class into small groups. Have the students refer to their Foldables to discuss the benefits of physical activity on social and mental/emotional health. Ask them to list ways that physical activity can influence the other two dimensions of health. They can list the benefits of each in two circles, one labeled social and the other labeled mental/emotional.

Alternative Activities for Chapter 5

ANALYZING INFLUENCES

Have students create a new three-tab concept map Foldable to help them establish their own fitness goals. Title the Foldable "My Fitness Goals." Guide students to consider the following: "What do I want to accomplish?" "Where do I begin?" and "What do I enjoy?" As students read and discuss the chapter, remind them to answer these questions honestly. Once the students have answered the questions, ask them to use their responses to write a short essay stating the "Why" and "How" of their commitment to these physical fitness goals.

ANALYZING

Have students create a new three-tab concept map Foldable to help them describe their experiences with three different physical activities. At the beginning of the week students should select three activities that they agree to try. After completing each activity, students should record their feeling about each activity under the appropriate tabs. By the end of the week, students should have a better idea of which physical activity best suites their lifestyle, interest, and personal physical fitness goals. Have some students share their thoughts, as this can have a positive influence on them or they may offer helpful information to other classmates.

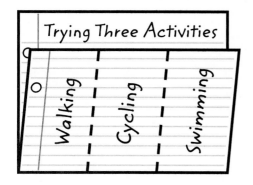

Student Study Tip

Remind students that note taking is a valuable skill and necessary for success in school. Learning to take notes requires practice, but can be rewarding down the road. Sometimes we write notes, put them away and later don't understand what we meant. Explain to students the importance of thinking before writing. Some important things to remember when taking notes is to include the main points and minor points, and leave space after these for later thoughts or details.

Course 1

FOLDABLES

Personal Health

CHAPTER SUMMARY

Healthy teeth and gums require regular brushing, flossing, and dental checkups. Healthy skin must be kept clean and protected from the sun. Cleanliness is also important for healthy hair, as is combing and brushing. Protecting eyes and ears will help safeguard vision and hearing. When buying health products, it's important to compare brands and prices and to read labels. Buyers must be alert to misleading ads or false claims. Health professionals are available in every community for regular checkups and specialty care.

CHAPTER PREVIEW

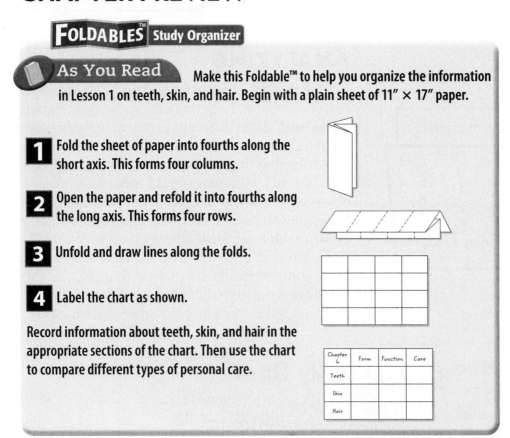

FOLDABLES™ Study Organizer

As You Read Make this Foldable™ to help you organize the information in Lesson 1 on teeth, skin, and hair. Begin with a plain sheet of 11" × 17" paper.

1 Fold the sheet of paper into fourths along the short axis. This forms four columns.

2 Open the paper and refold it into fourths along the long axis. This forms four rows.

3 Unfold and draw lines along the folds.

4 Label the chart as shown.

Record information about teeth, skin, and hair in the appropriate sections of the chart. Then use the chart to compare different types of personal care.

Chapter 6	Form	Function	Care
Teeth			
Skin			
Hair			

CHAPTER REVIEW

Foldables Follow-Up Activity

Have students use their Foldable chart to set both short-term and long-term goals for the care of teeth, skin, and hair. For example, their goals for teeth may include more regular brushing, using an improved toothpaste, and scheduling a dental checkup.

Alternative Activities for Chapter 6

EVALUATING

Have students complete the first three steps of the Foldable instructions. Have them use the Foldable to compare three brands of one personal-care product, such as shampoo. Have them label the chart columns with the product brand names; have them fill in the rows with each product's price, size, and benefits. Have them use the information to create an advertisement for the product that they feel is the best according to their comparisons.

	Brand A	Brand B	Brand C
Price			
Size			
Benefits			

	Specialty A	Specialty B	Specialty C
Condition			
Have I Ever Visited?			
Would I Like to Be?			

INVESTIGATING

Have students complete the first three steps of the Foldable instructions. Have them choose three of the medical specialties described on page 165 of the Student Edition. Have them label the chart rows with the specialties they have chosen. Have them fill in the columns with the conditions each specialty treats, whether they have ever visited that type of specialist, and whether they might like to be that kind of specialist as a career.

Student Study Tip

Encourage students to find a "study buddy." This is someone, such as a classmate or tutor, who can be part of their support system. Study buddies help each other understand assignments or think through difficult-to-understand concepts. Students who are ill and miss class can also call their study buddy to find out about homework assignments. Tell students that a study buddy is someone who would be on a list of their most reliable friends.

Course 1

FOLDABLES

Your Body Systems

CHAPTER SUMMARY

Cells, tissues, and organs make up our body systems. These systems work together to perform all the necessary bodily tasks. Body systems include the skeletal and muscular systems, the circulatory system, the respiratory system, the nervous system, and the digestive system. Physical, mental/emotional, and social changes occur during adolescence. Heredity is the process by which parents pass traits to their children. The life cycle includes infancy; childhood; and early, middle, and late adulthood.

CHAPTER PREVIEW

As You Read   Make this Foldable™ to help you organize the information on the form and function of body systems in Lesson 1. Begin with a plain sheet of 8½″ × 11″ paper.

1 Fold a sheet of paper along the long axis. Leave a ½″ tab along the side.

2 Turn the paper. Fold in half, then fold in half again.

3 Unfold and cut the top layer along the three fold lines. This makes four tabs.

4 Turn the paper vertically, and label the tabs as shown.

Write down the definitions of the terms *cells, tissues, organs*, and *body systems*, and list examples of each under the appropriate tab.

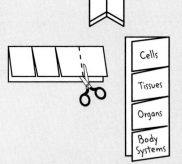

CHAPTER REVIEW

Foldables Follow-Up Activity

After students have completed their Foldable and have listed examples of body systems, ask them to identify the purpose of each system they've listed. Have students create a colorful drawing or display showing how body systems are composed of organs, organs are composed of tissues, and tissues are composed of cells. Ask them to label the different parts.

Alternative Activities for Chapter 7

DESCRIBING

Have students complete the first three steps of the Foldable instructions. Have students label the tabs with the different parts of the digestive system given on page 186 of the Student Edition, listing two on each tab. Inside the Foldable, have students draw a flow chart showing how the digestive system works. Flow charts should detail the process of digestion.

Salivary Glands and Esophagus

Liver and Stomach

Gallbladder and Pancreas

Small Intestine and Colon

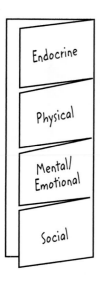

Endocrine

Physical

Mental/ Emotional

Social

PROBLEM SOLVING

Have students complete the first three steps of the Foldable instructions. On the four tabs, have them list the four types of development that occur during adolescence: endocrine, physical, mental/emotional, and social. Under each tab, have students note the appropriate changes that take place.

Student Study Tip

Remind students that they can't win at a board game if they're not sitting at the table with the other players. They can't do well in school if they don't show up or don't pay attention in class. While they're skipping class or being inattentive, the game continues without them. If they must miss class for legitimate reasons, encourage them to obtain the assignments ahead of time, if possible, or to arrange to make up the work afterward.

Course 1

Growth and Development

CHAPTER SUMMARY

The body system that makes it possible to create babies is the reproductive system. Like all body systems, the reproductive system needs proper care, which includes good hygiene. Heredity is the way in which parents pass certain traits, like body shape or hair color, to their children. Adolescence is a time of change in all areas of the health triangle. The stages of the life cycle are: infancy, childhood, adolescence, early adulthood, middle adulthood, and late adulthood.

CHAPTER PREVIEW

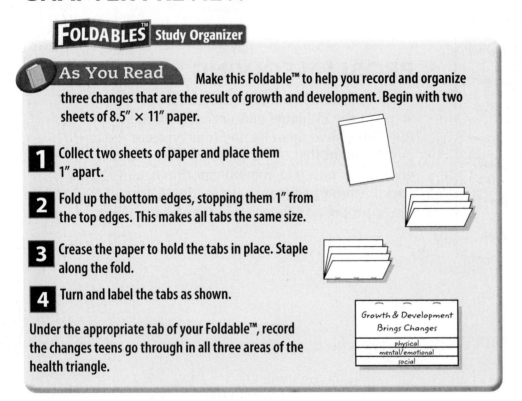

FOLDABLES™ Study Organizer

As You Read Make this Foldable™ to help you record and organize three changes that are the result of growth and development. Begin with two sheets of 8.5" × 11" paper.

1 Collect two sheets of paper and place them 1" apart.

2 Fold up the bottom edges, stopping them 1" from the top edges. This makes all tabs the same size.

3 Crease the paper to hold the tabs in place. Staple along the fold.

4 Turn and label the tabs as shown.

Under the appropriate tab of your Foldable™, record the changes teens go through in all three areas of the health triangle.

> Growth & Development
> Brings Changes
> physical
> mental/emotional
> social

CHAPTER REVIEW

Foldables Follow-Up Activity

Divide the class into small groups. Have the students refer to their Foldables to discuss the changes involving the three aspects of health they will probably go through in the next stages of life. How can you prepare for some of the changes you will go through?

Alternative Activities for Chapter 8

SYNTHESIZING

Have students create a new Foldable and title it "Reproduction." They should label the remaining tabs "Male," "Female," and "Fetus." Have them list the biological functions of reproduction on the tabs. They should explain what each brings to the reproduction process. In the "Fetus" tab, students should describe its development using the "Male" and "Female" information in the textbook.

Reproduction

| Male |
| Female |
| Fetus |

INVESTIGATING

Have students create a new Foldable titled "Heredity and Traits." Have students label the remaining tabs "Mother," "Father," and "Other family members." Have them think about the physical characteristics they or someone they know shares with their family members. Under each tab, list the first name of the person and the physical traits that person shares with their family member. They can list names and physical characteristics shared between other family members, using the "Other family members" tab. Have students share their information with the class.

Heredity and Traits

| Mother |
| Father |
| Other Family Members |

Student Study Tip

Encourage students to build their vocabulary. Have students select a new word from a dictionary everyday and use it that day in conversation or writing. Students can choose to keep a log of their new words. Everyday they should write their new word and its meaning on paper. They may want to include a sentence using their new word. This can be very helpful with remembering what the word means and how to use it correctly.

Course 1

FOLDABLES

Tobacco

CHAPTER SUMMARY

Tobacco contains nicotine, an addictive substance. Its other dangerous substances include tar and carbon monoxide. The chemicals in tobacco harm many parts of the body. Chewing tobacco and snuff are no safer than tobacco that is smoked. Secondhand smoke is tobacco smoke that stays in the air and is inhaled by nonsmokers. Teens may be under considerable pressure to smoke; however, most do not use tobacco. There are many ways and reasons to say no to tobacco.

CHAPTER PREVIEW

FOLDABLES™ Study Organizer

As You Read Make this Foldable™ to help you organize information in Lesson 1 on the harmful effects of tobacco. Begin with a plain sheet of 8½″ × 11″ paper.

1 Fold a sheet of paper in half along the short axis.

2 Open and fold the bottom edge up to form a pocket. Glue the edges.

3 Label the cover as shown. Label the pockets "Causes" and "Effects." Place an index card or quarter sheet of notebook paper into each pocket.

List and describe the causes and effects of tobacco addiction on the index cards or sheets of notebook paper cut into quarter sections. Store these cards in the appropriate pockets of your Foldable™.

CHAPTER REVIEW

Foldables Follow-Up Activity

After students have completed their Foldable, ask them to arrange an interview with an adult who is a nonsmoker. Have them prepare a list of questions based on the causes and effects of tobacco addiction noted in their Foldable. Did the person smoke in the past? Was the person pressured to smoke? If so, how did he or she resist? Have students report on their findings to the class. What personal characteristics did their subject seem to have that enabled the person to resist tobacco?

Alternative Activities for Chapter 9

REVIEWING

Have students complete the first two steps of the Foldable instructions. Have students label the pockets "Pressures" and "Refusal Skills." Have them insert into the appropriate pocket note cards or quarter sheets of notebook paper listing pressures to smoke and refusal skills. When they've finished, ask them to write an acrostic poem based on the first letters of key words indicating types of pressures: Media, Peers, Family, Stress, Weight.

	Most Effective?
Say No	
Tell Why	
Offer Options	
Promptly Leave	

ANALYZING

Referring to the Foldable students made for the Reviewing activity, have students make a table listing the refusal skills. Have them poll at least 25 students at school, asking their peers which refusal skill they think is most effective. They should then graph the results of the poll.

Student Study Tip

Ask students where they do their homework at home. Do they have a special place to study? A study spot should be comfortable, have a smooth surface for writing and for spreading papers out, have good lighting, be free of clutter, and be reasonably peaceful and quiet. Students should keep enough supplies on hand nearby, as well as dictionaries, other resources, and a wastebasket.

Course 1

FOLDABLES

Alcohol and Other Drugs

CHAPTER SUMMARY

Drugs are substances that change the structure or function of the body or mind. Alcohol is a drug. It affects the brain, the blood vessels, the heart, the liver, and the stomach. Medicines are drugs that cure or prevent disease. The Food and Drug Administration reviews all drugs sold in the United States to be sure they are safe. Medicines and other drugs are sometimes misused. Drug abuse can lead to addiction. Saying no to substance abuse can help teens feel good and look their best. They should seek healthy alternatives to drug and alcohol use.

CHAPTER PREVIEW

FOLDABLES™ Study Organizer

As You Read Make this Foldable™ to record information on alcohol and its harmful effects, presented in Lesson 1. Begin with two sheets of notebook paper.

1 Fold one sheet in half from top to bottom. Cut about 1" along the fold at both ends, stopping at the margin lines.

2 Fold the second sheet in half from top to bottom. Cut the fold between the margin lines.

3 Insert the first sheet through the second sheet and align folds.

4 Fold the bound pages in half to make a booklet, and label the cover as shown. Then label each page as instructed by your teacher.

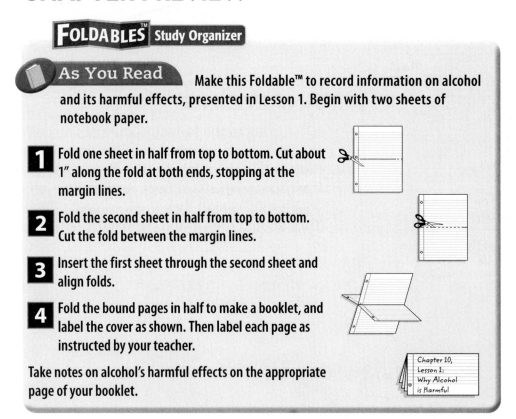

Chapter 10, Lesson 1: Why Alcohol is Harmful

Take notes on alcohol's harmful effects on the appropriate page of your booklet.

CHAPTER REVIEW

Foldables Follow-Up Activity

Ask someone from local law enforcement to speak to the class about the dangers of drinking and driving. Ask students to prepare a list of questions for the speaker based on the information in their Foldable.

Alternative Activities for Chapter 10

ANALYZING INFLUENCES

Have students follow the Foldable instructions to create a booklet foldable. They should label the first three pages with the following titles: "Drug Safety," "Using Medicines Safely," and "The Misuse and Abuse of Drugs." Have them note important points from the text under each topic.

While watching TV at home for one hour, students should record the number of times drugs are advertised and the names of these drugs. On the remaining pages in their Foldable, students should write their opinions about the effects of advertising on drug misuse and abuse. Ask them to give reasons to support their opinions.

Drug Safety
Using Medicines Safely
The Misuse and Abuse of Drugs

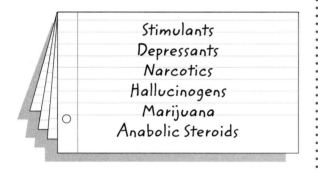

Stimulants
Depressants
Narcotics
Hallucinogens
Marijuana
Anabolic Steroids

INVESTIGATING

Have students follow the Foldable instructions to create a booklet Foldable. Have them label the pages with the following titles: "Stimulants," "Depressants," "Narcotics, Hallucinogens," "Marijuana," and "Anabolic Steroids." Have them take notes on the damage caused by each type of drug on the appropriate page. When they've finished, have them research the kinds of resources available to help people who are addicted overcome their dependencies.

Student Study Tip

Students can improve their reading comprehension by surveying a passage to look for clues to its subject. What is the title of the passage? Are there any pictures, tables, or charts? What do the captions say? What information is given in the headings and subheadings? Students may already know a little bit about the topic. Does their prior knowledge help them predict what this new material will be about?

Course 1

FOLDABLES

Preventing Diseases

CHAPTER SUMMARY

Communicable diseases are those that can be spread from person to person. The immune system fights the pathogens that cause disease. Disease prevention involves practicing healthy behaviors and being vaccinated. Sexually transmitted diseases (STDs) are spread by sexual contact. Abstinence is the best way to prevent STDs. Noncommunicable diseases can be present at birth, or they can be caused by unhealthy lifestyles or environmental factors. They include heart disease, cancer, allergies, asthma, and diabetes.

CHAPTER PREVIEW

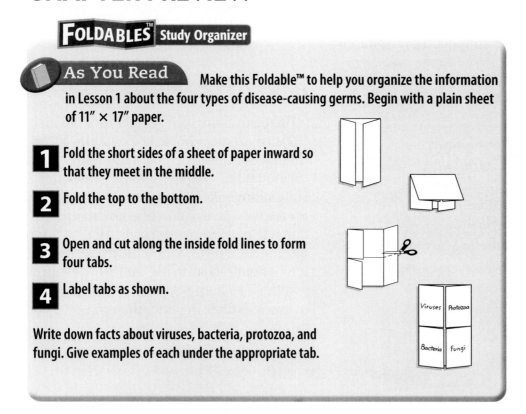

FOLDABLES™ Study Organizer

As You Read Make this Foldable™ to help you organize the information in Lesson 1 about the four types of disease-causing germs. Begin with a plain sheet of 11″ × 17″ paper.

1 Fold the short sides of a sheet of paper inward so that they meet in the middle.

2 Fold the top to the bottom.

3 Open and cut along the inside fold lines to form four tabs.

4 Label tabs as shown.

Write down facts about viruses, bacteria, protozoa, and fungi. Give examples of each under the appropriate tab.

Viruses | Protozoa
Bacteria | Fungi

CHAPTER REVIEW

Foldables Follow-Up Activity

Make arrangements with your school's science teacher to show students examples of some of the larger organisms, such as bacteria, protozoa, or fungi, under a microscope. Have students describe what they saw. They can write their descriptions on their Foldable or on a separate sheet of paper.

Alternative Activities for Chapter 11

RESEARCHING

Have students complete the first three steps of the Foldable instructions. Then have students label each tab with the names of two vaccines listed in the Student Edition. Inside, have them note the diseases treated by each vaccine. When they've finished, ask them to research and write a report on a well-known battle against disease, such as the discovery of penicillin, development of the polio vaccine, work done to find the source of malaria during the building of the Panama Canal, or the efforts of the World Health Organization against smallpox in the 1960s and 1970s.

Hep B and DTaP

Hib and IPV

PCV and MMR

Varicella and Hep A

1. Soap and Warm Water

2. Wash Around Fingernails and Creases

3. Rinse

4. Dry

ORGANIZING

Have students complete the first three steps of the Foldable instructions. Then have students label the tabs with the steps for handwashing given on page 276 of the Student Edition. Have them organize their notes about the different steps inside the Foldable. When they've finished, ask students to name other steps they can take to prevent communicable diseases.

Student Study Tip

Remind students that mapping and outlining are two ways of organizing notes and other material. For mapping, they should divide the paper into sections and jot down related words or phrases in the proper area. Mapping is useful for creative thinking and making notes during brainstorming. The outline begins with a major idea. Major points about the topic follow. Subpoints and supporting details back up the major points. Outlining is more precise and well suited to formal reports. Provide examples of maps and outlines for students.

Course 1

FOLDABLES

Safety and the Environment

CHAPTER SUMMARY

The accident chain is a sequence of events that can lead to accidental injury. Many accidents can be prevented if people develop safe habits. In an emergency, it's important to check the scene and the victim, call for help, and care for the victim until help arrives. First aid is the care given to an injured or ill person before regular medical care arrives. Air, water, and land pollution can threaten health. Using resources wisely can help reduce pollution.

CHAPTER PREVIEW

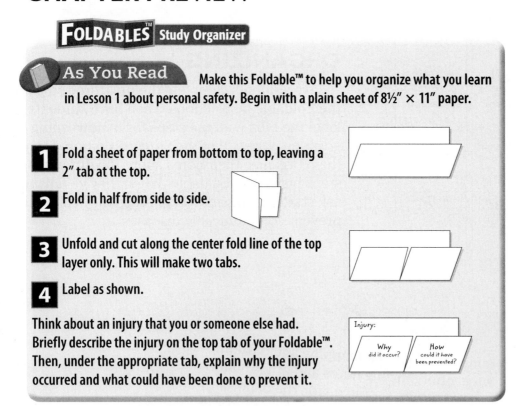

FOLDABLES™ Study Organizer

As You Read Make this Foldable™ to help you organize what you learn in Lesson 1 about personal safety. Begin with a plain sheet of 8½" × 11" paper.

1 Fold a sheet of paper from bottom to top, leaving a 2" tab at the top.

2 Fold in half from side to side.

3 Unfold and cut along the center fold line of the top layer only. This will make two tabs.

4 Label as shown.

Think about an injury that you or someone else had. Briefly describe the injury on the top tab of your Foldable™. Then, under the appropriate tab, explain why the injury occurred and what could have been done to prevent it.

Injury:

Why did it occur? How could it have been prevented?

CHAPTER REVIEW

Foldables Follow-Up Activity

Referring to the incident described in their Foldable, ask students to write a one-page short story, create a short poem or song, or make a poster illustrating the idea that "Safety Is an Attitude."

Alternative Activities for Chapter 12

APPLYING

Have students complete the first three steps of the Foldable instructions. Have them label the top tab "Preventive Steps." Have them label the right tab "Safety at Home." Have them label the left tab "Safety on the Road." Under each tab, students should list preventive steps to take for safety in each location. When they've finished, they should write on an index card a list of phone numbers to call in an emergency and place it near their phone at home.

Preventive Steps

Safety on the Road

Safety at Home

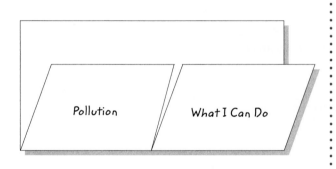

Pollution

What I Can Do

ANALYZING

Have students complete the first three steps of the Foldable instructions. Ask students to label one tab, "Pollution" and the other tab "What I Can Do." Under the first tab, students should list the types of pollution and the harm each type of pollution can cause. Under the other tab, students should indicate steps they can take to reduce pollution.

Student Study Tip

Some students are nervous about taking tests. Adequate preparation can help prevent anxiety. Suggest that they ask their teachers what material will be covered on the test and what types of questions will be used. Essay questions may require broader understanding and fewer factual details than objective questions. Suggest that students study over several days and then review on the final day rather than cramming at the last minute. They should get enough sleep the night before, exercise to relieve tension, eat a good breakfast, and maintain a positive attitude.

Course 1

FOLDABLES

Understanding Health and Wellness

CHAPTER SUMMARY

Health is a combination of physical, mental/emotional, and social well-being. Keeping the three parts of the health triangle in balance is the best way to achieve good health. Both heredity and the environment affect a person's health, as do his or her health choices. Family, friends, and the media often influence those choices. Avoiding risk behaviors is important. Some risks are cumulative—when they are added together, their effects increase. Prevention is important to reducing and avoiding risks.

CHAPTER PREVIEW

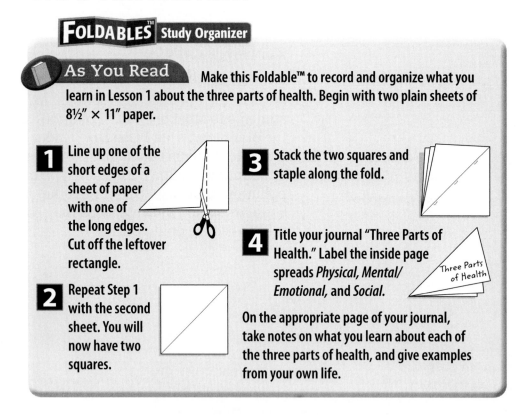

FOLDABLES™ Study Organizer

As You Read Make this Foldable™ to record and organize what you learn in Lesson 1 about the three parts of health. Begin with two plain sheets of 8½" × 11" paper.

1 Line up one of the short edges of a sheet of paper with one of the long edges. Cut off the leftover rectangle.

2 Repeat Step 1 with the second sheet. You will now have two squares.

3 Stack the two squares and staple along the fold.

4 Title your journal "Three Parts of Health." Label the inside page spreads *Physical, Mental/Emotional,* and *Social.*

Three Parts of Health

On the appropriate page of your journal, take notes on what you learn about each of the three parts of health, and give examples from your own life.

CHAPTER REVIEW

Foldables Follow-Up Activity

Divide the class into small groups. Write on the board: "When you can't change your situation, try to change your perception of the situation." Define *perception* for students in this context as the way they think about or understand a situation. Ask students to discuss what this statement means in terms of the notes in their Foldables and what they've learned in this chapter.

Alternative Activities for Chapter 1

COMPARE AND CONTRAST

Have students create a new Foldable. Have them label the first page "Heredity." Halfway through the Foldable (about on page 3), have them begin a new section titled "Environment." Then ask them to list in the appropriate section the influences of each factor on health and give examples. Then ask volunteers to research recent studies done with identical twins. Ask them to report back to the class on what scientists have learned about heredity versus environment in the studies.

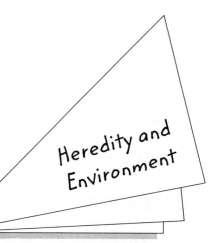

Heredity and Environment

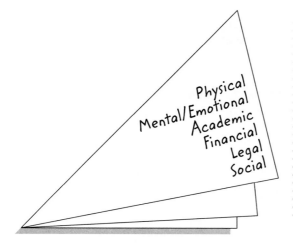

Physical
Mental/Emotional
Academic
Financial
Legal
Social

ANALYZING

Ask students to create a new Foldable. Have them write the six consequences of risk behaviors on its pages and give an example of each. After they've finished, discuss with the class a recent action movie that is popular, especially one based on a comic book character. What effect does watching such a film have on risk behaviors?

Student Study Tip

Encourage students to become familiar with their textbooks so that they can find things more easily. Point out the different features in each lesson. Ask them to describe how the Index is organized. What about index subheads? When looking for the causes of diabetes, would they be most likely to find it under *causes* or *diabetes?* What does it mean when an entry says *See also...* followed by another entry?

Course 2

FOLDABLES

Taking Charge of Your Health

CHAPTER SUMMARY

Decision-making, goal setting, and analyzing influences are health skills that support each part of the health triangle. The H.E.L.P. criteria can evaluate decisions, while goal setting encourages good decision-making. A person's character is the way he or she thinks and acts. Trustworthiness, respect, responsibility, fairness, caring, and citizenship are all traits of good character.

CHAPTER PREVIEW

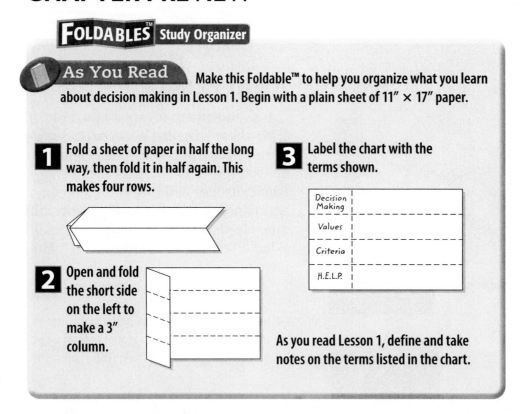

FOLDABLES™ Study Organizer

As You Read — Make this Foldable™ to help you organize what you learn about decision making in Lesson 1. Begin with a plain sheet of 11″ × 17″ paper.

1 Fold a sheet of paper in half the long way, then fold it in half again. This makes four rows.

2 Open and fold the short side on the left to make a 3″ column.

3 Label the chart with the terms shown.

Decision Making	
Values	
Criteria	
H.E.L.P.	

As you read Lesson 1, define and take notes on the terms listed in the chart.

CHAPTER REVIEW

Foldables Follow-Up Activity

Have students use their Foldables and the text to write a one-page summary of Chapter 2. Tell them to be sure to use all the vocabulary terms included in the chapter.

Alternative Activities for Chapter 2

INTERVIEWING

Have students create a new Foldable. Have them list the H.E.L.P. criteria in the left column: "Healthful," "Ethical," "Legal," and "Parent Approval." In the right column, have them write examples of ways they could use these criteria. Then ask students to interview someone they know with good character about an important decision the person made and what values came into play.

Healthful	
Ethical	
Legal	
Parent Approval	

DECISION MAKING

Have students create a new Foldable. In the left column they should list four decisions they must make during the next 24 hours. They should keep the decisions simple, such as whether to watch TV or call a friend. In the right column they should give an example of how they used the steps of the decision-making process to arrive at their final decisions.

Student Study Tip

Explain to students that people with a positive attitude almost always do better in school. A positive attitude often arises from simple, everyday behaviors that signal self-respect and respect for others. List the following aids to a positive attitude on the board:

1. When you talk to people, make eye contact.
2. Learn the names of all the teachers and staff in your school and greet them.
3. Say please and thank you.
4. Don't be a quitter.
5. Accept the fact that you will make some mistakes.

Course 2

Physical Activity and Fitness

CHAPTER SUMMARY

Physical activity is any kind of movement that causes the body to use energy. It builds strength, endurance, and flexibility. The skeletal and muscular systems support the body and enable it to move. The circulatory system transports essential materials throughout the body and removes wastes. Preventing injuries, eating healthfully, and avoiding overtraining and harmful substances help a person stay in shape.

CHAPTER PREVIEW

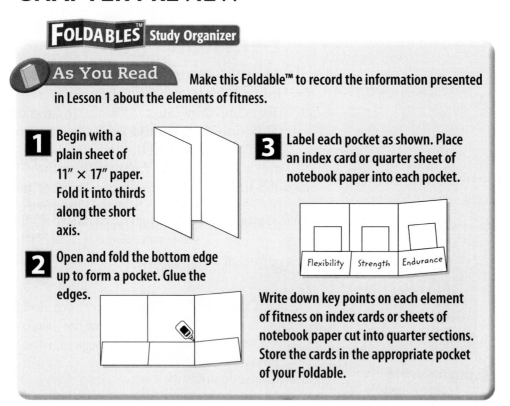

FOLDABLES™ Study Organizer

As You Read Make this Foldable™ to record the information presented in Lesson 1 about the elements of fitness.

1 Begin with a plain sheet of 11″ × 17″ paper. Fold it into thirds along the short axis.

2 Open and fold the bottom edge up to form a pocket. Glue the edges.

3 Label each pocket as shown. Place an index card or quarter sheet of notebook paper into each pocket.

Flexibility | Strength | Endurance

Write down key points on each element of fitness on index cards or sheets of notebook paper cut into quarter sections. Store the cards in the appropriate pocket of your Foldable.

CHAPTER REVIEW

Foldables Follow-Up Activity

On a sheet of paper, have students note information about the skeletal, muscular, and circulatory systems. Using their Foldables for reference, they should then indicate how the three elements of fitness relate to each system.

Alternative Activities for Chapter 3

EVALUATING

Have students create a new Foldable, labeling the pockets "Achieving Fitness Goals," "Elements of a Good Workout," and "Checking Your Progress." Have them create cards noting important information about each category. When they've finished, ask them to review at least one popular health magazine. Ask them to write an evaluation of the magazine's information on fitness based on what they've learned so far in class.

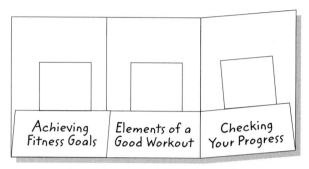

ANALYZING

Have students create a new Foldable and label the pockets "Preventing Injuries," "Sports Nutrition," and "Avoiding Harmful Substances." Have them make cards with important information for each category. When they've finished, discuss as a class the role of team spirit in these categories and in building mental/emotional health. How could they encourage someone with limited athletic ability to join in?

Student Study Tip

Discuss with students how staying organized can help them stay on schedule, accomplish more work in less time, and avoid stress. In their notebooks or backpacks they should keep a class schedule and notebook for assignments, a small calendar, supplies needed for class such as pencils and paper, storage for computer disks, a small ruler, a folder for protecting papers, and a list of important phone numbers.

Course 2

Nutrition

CHAPTER SUMMARY

Nutrients are substances in food that the body needs in order to grow, have energy, and stay healthy. Making sensible food choices includes avoiding those that contain too much fat, sugar, or salt. The Food Guide Pyramid can aid in making sensible choices. Healthy eating should include breakfast and nutritious snacks. The digestive system turns food into fuel and removes wastes from the body. Eating disorders are extreme behaviors that can lead to illness or death.

CHAPTER PREVIEW

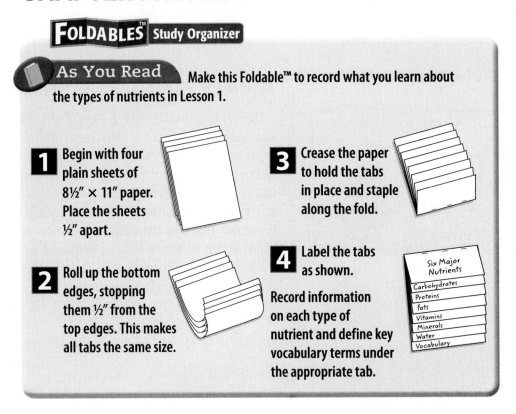

FOLDABLES™ Study Organizer

As You Read Make this Foldable™ to record what you learn about the types of nutrients in Lesson 1.

1 Begin with four plain sheets of 8½" × 11" paper. Place the sheets ½" apart.

2 Roll up the bottom edges, stopping them ½" from the top edges. This makes all tabs the same size.

3 Crease the paper to hold the tabs in place and staple along the fold.

4 Label the tabs as shown.

Record information on each type of nutrient and define key vocabulary terms under the appropriate tab.

Six Major Nutrients
Carbohydrates
Proteins
Fats
Vitamins
Minerals
Water
Vocabulary

CHAPTER REVIEW

Foldables Follow-Up Activity

Have students create an e-zine or printed newsletter about nutrition based on the information in their Foldables and what they've learned so far in class. Suggest that they make their publication entertaining and filled with interesting facts, recipes, and hints for a healthier life. If they enjoy the activity, you may want them to continue it with new material as the course progresses.

Alternative Activities for Chapter 4

SHARING INFORMATION

Have students create a new Foldable labeled with the six divisions of MyPyramid and "Additional Notes." Ask them to use the Foldable to make notes as they read the chapter. When they've finished, have them divide into smaller groups. Each group should make an enlarged version of the Foldable with information from different sections of this chapter. Have them display these larger Foldables on a bulletin board in the school cafeteria where other students can benefit from the information.

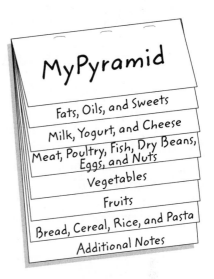

MyPyramid
- Fats, Oils, and Sweets
- Milk, Yogurt, and Cheese
- Meat, Poultry, Fish, Dry Beans, Eggs, and Nuts
- Vegetables
- Fruits
- Bread, Cereal, Rice, and Pasta
- Additional Notes

Parts of the Digestive/
Excretory Systems
- Esophagus
- Stomach
- Small Intestine
- Liver
- Gallbladder
- Pancreas
- Colon

INVESTIGATING

Have students create a new Foldable labeled "Stomach," "Small Intestine," "Liver," "Gallbladder," "Pancreas," and "Colon." Under each tab they should include information about that particular part of the digestive or excretory system. When they've finished, ask for volunteers to create and share with the class a snack or other food item containing an ingredient some students may not have tried before, such as soy.

Student Study Tip

Arrange for students to visit the library for a short refresher on how to use its resources. Discuss with them the way nonfiction books are organized according to call numbers. Most libraries post on a bank of shelves the number range stored on those shelves. Review how to read the numbers, which include the first letters of the author's name.

Course 2

FOLDABLES

Mental and Emotional Health

CHAPTER SUMMARY

Mental/emotional health is the ability to deal in a reasonable way with the stresses and changes of daily life. Expressing emotions in healthy ways, coping with change, and avoiding unhealthful behaviors all lead to improved health. Stress can be positive or negative. Negative stress can be avoided or managed. Mental and emotional problems include anxiety disorders and mood disorders. Teens with mental or emotional problems should seek help.

CHAPTER PREVIEW

As You Read   Make this Foldable™ to help you record what you learn about mental and emotional health in Lesson 1. Begin with a plain sheet of 8½″ × 11″ paper.

1 Line up one of the short edges of the sheet of paper with one of the long edges to form a triangle. Fold and cut off the leftover rectangle.

3 Cut up one fold line and stop in the middle. Draw an X on one tab, and label the other three as shown.

2 Fold the triangle in half, and unfold. The folds will form an X dividing four equal sections.

4 Fold the X flap under the other flap, and glue together to make a three-sided pyramid.

Take notes on the three factors that shape personality.

CHAPTER REVIEW

Foldables Follow-Up Activity

Discuss with the class how the factors that shape personality can also influence ways they express emotions and manage stress. Invite them to refer to their Foldables to create a "family tree" listing stress-management techniques used by family members or friends. If appropriate, ask them to consider which of the behaviors they use are like those of a family member or friend.

Alternative Activities for Chapter 5

EXPLAINING

Have students create a new Foldable. On the three sides of the pyramid they should write "Improving Self-Esteem and Self-Confidence," "Respecting Individual Differences," and "Attitudes and Behavior." In the appropriate spaces they should note the ways in which these factors influence mental and emotional health. When students are finished, write the following statement on the board: "Respect makes you feel confident and trusting." Ask students to write a one-page essay on what the statement means to them.

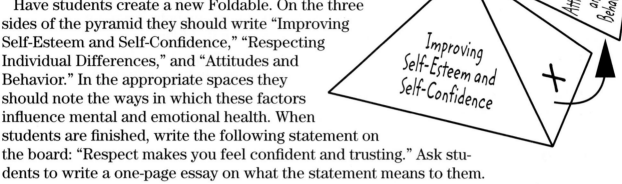

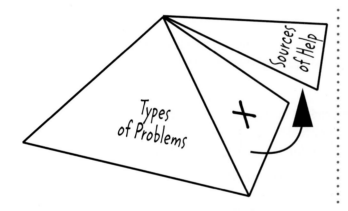

ORGANIZING

Have students create a new Foldable. Have them label the sides as follows: "Types of Problems," "Warning Signs," and "Sources of Help." They should then make notes about each category in the appropriate space. When students have finished, discuss crisis intervention hot lines. Ask them to research hot lines available in their community.

Student Study Tip

Encourage students to make a homework planner to help them organize their time. This is a chart with the days of the week written at the top and the times devoted to study written along the side. The times should include only those hours available for homework, not hours spent in school. Students should then plan their week depending on what work they must accomplish. For example, the entry for Monday from 4:00 to 5:00 might say "Study with Jane for health test." The planner should also include other activities that might interfere with normal study hours, such as a dental checkup, so students will not forget that those hours will not be available.

Course 2

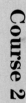

FOLDABLES

Building Healthy Relationships

CHAPTER SUMMARY

Communication is an exchange of thoughts, feelings, and beliefs among people. Families nurture their members; however, family life involves changes and challenges. Trustworthiness, caring, and respect are the basis for most friendships. Peer pressure can influence how people think and act. Abstinence is not participating in unsafe behaviors. Refusal skills are ways to say no to risk behaviors.

CHAPTER PREVIEW

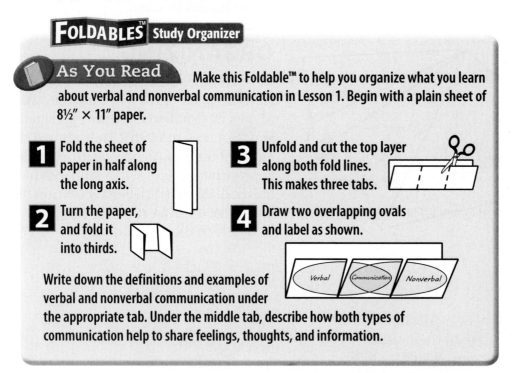

FOLDABLES™ Study Organizer

As You Read Make this Foldable™ to help you organize what you learn about verbal and nonverbal communication in Lesson 1. Begin with a plain sheet of 8½" × 11" paper.

1 Fold the sheet of paper in half along the long axis.

2 Turn the paper, and fold it into thirds.

3 Unfold and cut the top layer along both fold lines. This makes three tabs.

4 Draw two overlapping ovals and label as shown.

Verbal *Communication* *Nonverbal*

Write down the definitions and examples of verbal and nonverbal communication under the appropriate tab. Under the middle tab, describe how both types of communication help to share feelings, thoughts, and information.

CHAPTER REVIEW

Foldables Follow-Up Activity

Ask students to suggest situations in which speaking and listening strategies are especially important. Have volunteers role-play several situations and demonstrate both verbal and nonverbal communication. Discuss with the class any special influences at work in each situation, such as peer pressure.

Alternative Activities for Chapter 6

EVALUATING

Have students create a new Foldable. On the left and right tabs they should write "Positive Peer Pressure" and "Negative Peer Pressure." Under these tabs they should give examples of each type. On the center tab they should write

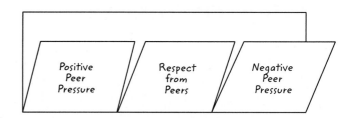

"Respect from Peers" and under it indicate ways in which peer pressure can cause teens to do things that affect the respect received from peers. As homework, if appropriate, students might ask older family members about kinds of peer pressure they faced when they were teens.

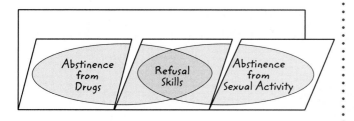

ANALYZING

Have students create a new Foldable. They should label the tabs from left to right "Abstinence from Drugs," "Refusal Skills," and "Abstinence from Sexual Activity." They should then list the benefits of abstinence under the left and right tabs. Under the center tab they should list refusal skills that apply to each type of abstinence. When they've finished, ask them to use the information to create an advertisement for abstinence.

Student Study Tip

Encourage students to think about their study sequence. Several sequences can be used: hardest things first, easiest things first, least important to most important, or a combination. Sometimes such things as an upcoming test will dictate the order, but sequencing based on personal preferences can result in a better use of study time. Suggest that students try several sequences to find the one that seems to work best for them.

Course 2

FOLDABLES

Resolving Conflicts and Preventing Violence

CHAPTER SUMMARY

A conflict is a disagreement between people with opposing viewpoints. Conflict can result from arguments, peer pressure, revenge, and prejudice. Nonviolent confrontation, negotiation, and peer mediation can help bring about a win-win situation. Many strategies can help prevent violence. Abuse is the physical, emotional, or mental mistreatment of another person. Victims of abuse need to get help.

CHAPTER PREVIEW

FOLDABLES™ Study Organizer

As You Read Make this Foldable™ to help you organize what you learn in Lesson 1 about the causes of conflict. Begin with a plain sheet of 11″ × 17″ paper.

1 Fold the sheet of paper into thirds along the short axis. This forms three columns.

2 Open the paper and refold into thirds along the long axis, then fold in half again lengthwise.

3 Unfold and draw lines along the folds.

4 Label the chart as shown.

As you read the lesson, fill in the chart with an example of a behavior that might escalate and de-escalate each type of conflict.

Cause	Escalation	De-escalation
Argument		
Peer Pressure		
Revenge		
Prejudice		
Additional Notes		

CHAPTER REVIEW

Foldables Follow-Up Activity

Divide the class into small groups. Have students refer to their Foldable to discuss conflict situations in which they've been involved. Was the conflict resolved successfully? If not, what might have been done differently?

Alternative Activities for Chapter 7

DEFINING

Have students create a new Foldable. Have them label the columns "Resolution Skill," "Definition," and "Example." Have them label the rows under "Resolution Skill" as follows: "Peaceful Resolution," "Negotiation," "Peer Mediation," "Win-Win," and "Additional Notes." Have them complete the chart by filling in the definition and an example for each skill. When they've finished, ask them to create posters illustrating conflict resolution.

Resolution Skill	Definition	Example
Peaceful Resolution		
Negotiation		
Peer Mediation		
Win-Win		
Additional Notes		

Causes	Prevention	Examples
Prejudice		
Weapons		
Peer Pressure		
Alcohol and Drugs		
Additional Notes		

IDENTIFYING

Have students make a new Foldable. Have them label the columns "Causes," "Prevention," and "Examples." Have them label the rows under "Causes" as follows: "Prejudice," "Weapons," "Peer Pressure," "Alcohol and Drugs," and "Additional Notes." Under "Prevention," have them identify steps they can take to prevent violence when each cause is present. Under the third column they should describe relevant examples. If possible, arrange for students to collaborate via the Internet with students in other schools in a violence-prevention project.

Student Study Tip

Review with students ways in which to get the most help from a dictionary. Point out where pronunciations and variant spellings are found in the entries. Help them find the pronunciation key, which is usually at the top or bottom of each page. Warn them about homographs—words that have the same spelling but different meanings. Are homographs listed under a single entry or in separate entries?

Course 2

FOLDABLES

79

Tobacco

CHAPTER SUMMARY

The dangerous substances in tobacco include nicotine, tar, and carbon monoxide. Tobacco poses a great risk to the normal functioning of the body. All the parts of the respiratory system work together to help a person breathe. Germs, tobacco smoke, chemicals, and environmental pollution can damage the respiratory system. Tobacco users form an addiction. An addiction involves both psychological and physical dependence. Tips and programs are available for kicking the tobacco habit; however, the best choice is never to use tobacco in the first place.

CHAPTER PREVIEW

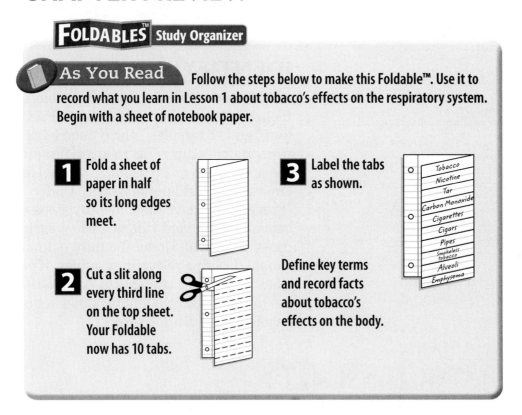

FOLDABLES™ Study Organizer

As You Read Follow the steps below to make this Foldable™. Use it to record what you learn in Lesson 1 about tobacco's effects on the respiratory system. Begin with a sheet of notebook paper.

1 Fold a sheet of paper in half so its long edges meet.

2 Cut a slit along every third line on the top sheet. Your Foldable now has 10 tabs.

3 Label the tabs as shown.

Define key terms and record facts about tobacco's effects on the body.

Tobacco
Nicotine
Tar
Carbon Monoxide
Cigarettes
Cigars
Pipes
Smokeless tobacco
Alveoli
Emphysema

CHAPTER REVIEW

Foldables Follow-Up Activity

Have students create a true-false test based on the information in their Foldable. Then have them ask at least ten people to take the test to find out whether or not people know the facts about tobacco. Ask them to graph the results.

Alternative Activities for Chapter 8

DEFINING

Have students create a new Foldable. On the tabs they should write these labels: "Respiratory System," "Epiglottis," "Trachea," "Bronchi," "Lungs," "Diaphragm," "Secondhand Smoke," "Mainstream Smoke," "Sidestream Smoke," and "Passive Smoker." Ask them to define the terms and note key facts. When they are finished, ask students to go online to identify advocacy groups for quitting tobacco use. What steps do the groups recommend?

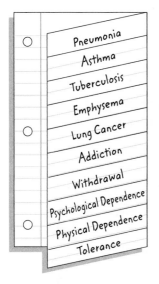

Respiratory System
Epiglottis
Trachea
Bronchi
Lungs
Diaphragm
Secondhand Smoke
Mainstream Smoke
Sidestream Smoke
Passive Smoker

Pneumonia
Asthma
Tuberculosis
Emphysema
Lung Cancer
Addiction
Withdrawal
Psychological Dependence
Physical Dependence
Tolerance

IDENTIFYING

Have students create a new Foldable. On the tabs they should write these labels: "Pneumonia," "Asthma," "Tuberculosis," "Emphysema," "Lung Cancer," "Addiction," "Withdrawal," "Psychological Dependence," "Physical Dependence," and "Tolerance." Ask them to define the terms and note key facts. If possible, ask a physician to visit and talk to the class about the link between smoking and lung cancer.

Student Study Tip

Suggest to students that they keep a record of their achievements in class and that they reward themselves when they succeed. A chart is useful for keeping track of grades and other achievements. But grades are only one aspect of success. Suggest that they note skills or topics they are struggling with and record goals met. For example, an entry might say "Worked with Juan and now I understand fractions!" You might let the class brainstorm possible rewards for meeting positive goals. Rewards do not have to be extravagant or cost money.

Course 2

FOLDABLES

Alcohol

CHAPTER SUMMARY

Alcohol is a drug and the most widely used and abused drug in the United States. It affects a person physically, mentally, and socially. Alcohol use can greatly harm a person's health. It is a depressant and a toxin to the body. The affects of alcohol on the body depend on the size, gender, and amount of alcohol consumed. Laws restricting alcohol use exist to protect the health, safety, and welfare of the public. The age restriction on alcohol use makes it illegal for teens to consume alcohol. Teens may try alcohol for several reasons such as, curiosity, to be popular, relaxation, to feel more grown-up, and to control emotions that they don't know how to handle. Teens can use refusals skills to say no and resist the pressures to drink alcohol.

CHAPTER PREVIEW

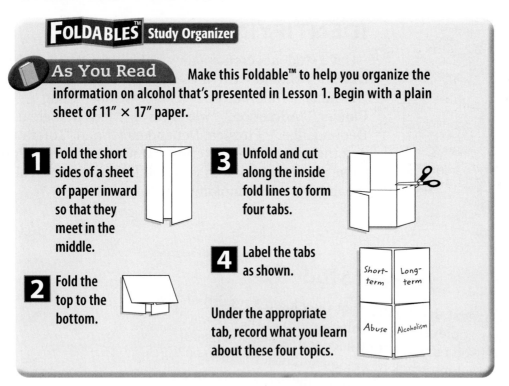

FOLDABLES™ Study Organizer

As You Read Make this Foldable™ to help you organize the information on alcohol that's presented in Lesson 1. Begin with a plain sheet of 11" × 17" paper.

1 Fold the short sides of a sheet of paper inward so that they meet in the middle.

2 Fold the top to the bottom.

3 Unfold and cut along the inside fold lines to form four tabs.

4 Label the tabs as shown.

Under the appropriate tab, record what you learn about these four topics.

Short-term | Long-term
Abuse | Alcoholism

CHAPTER REVIEW

Foldables Follow-Up Activity

Divide the class into small groups. Have the students refer to their Foldables to discuss how alcohol affects the three aspects of health. Following the students group discussions, ask students to tell you their answers and write them on the board.

Alternative Activities for Chapter 9

APPLYING KNOWLEDGE

Have students create a new Foldable and label the tabs "Scenario," "Peer pressure," "Reasons to refuse," and "Saying no to alcohol." Have them use a skit format and make a dialogue to refuse alcohol. You can provide a scenario or have the students make their own hypothetical situation involving peer pressure to drink alcohol. After students are done with their skit, ask volunteers to read their skit. On the board list their reasons to refuse and how they say no to use alcohol.

ANALYZING

Have students create a new Foldable to help them understand how the media portrays alcohol use and how laws restrict its use. Label the flaps of the Foldable "Radio," "T.V. commercials," "Movies," and "Alcohol use laws." Ask them to take notes as they read and discuss the material in class. When they are finished, divide students into groups and let them discuss and use the text to fill in their Foldable. Tell students they are to include the types of feelings and descriptions of characters that the different media types try to display. When students are done, have them write about how these influences affect their thoughts on alcohol use and what they can do to avoid media's influence. Have students share their opinions and thoughts with the class.

Student Study Tip

Discuss with the class the concept of time management. Time management is the skill of organizing, prioritizing, accomplishing and strategizing things that need to be done. This skill is one that most successful people have and use on a day-to-day bases. One important concept of time management is planning. Students can plan their work assignments and activities so that their time is used effectively. Encourage students to create and maintain a calendar or organizer for important dates.

Course 2

FOLDABLES

Drugs

CHAPTER SUMMARY

A drug is a substance other than food that changes the structure or function of the body or mind. Medicines are drugs that prevent or cure illnesses or ease their symptoms. Alcohol is a drug that has both short- and long-term effects on body systems. Drug abuse is the use of a drug for nonmedical purposes. Abused drugs include marijuana, stimulants, and depressants. The nervous system is the body's control center. Alcohol and other drugs expose people to physical, mental/emotional, and social risks.

CHAPTER PREVIEW

As You Read Make this Foldable™ to help you organize the main ideas on drug use and abuse in Lesson 1. Begin with four circles of paper: one large (8" across), one medium (7" across), and two small (each 2½" across).

1 Fold the medium circle in half. Glue the top half onto the large circle, making sure that the bottoms of the two circles are aligned. This will create a tab from the unglued part of the medium circle.

2 Fold the two small circles in half. Glue the top half of each circle onto the bottom half of the medium circle. This will create two more tabs.

3 Label as shown.

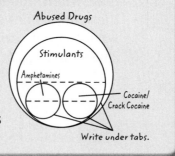

Abused Drugs

Stimulants

Amphetamines

Cocaine/
Crack Cocaine

Write under tabs.

Under the appropriate tab, define key terms and record information on abused drugs.

CHAPTER REVIEW

Foldables Follow-Up Activity

Ask a pharmacist to speak to the class about differences between prescription and over-the-counter medicines. Ask the person to discuss safety precautions taken when dispensing drugs and the effects of advertising prescription drugs to consumers. Have students prepare questions for the speaker ahead of time based on the information in their Foldable.

Alternative Activities for Chapter 10

ANALYZING

Have students create a new Foldable to help them understand the affects of drug abuse on the three areas of health. Have them label the large circle "Drug Abuse," the medium-sized circle "Physical Health," and the small circles "Mental/Emotional Health," and "Social Health." Ask them to write general information about drug abuse on the back of the large circle and specific information about how drug abuse affects the areas of health under each tab. When they've finished, ask them to organize notes on the rest of the chapter's information using a standard outline form.

Drug Abuse

Physical Health

Mental/Emotional Health   Social Health

Write under tabs.

APPLYING

Have students create a new Foldable. Have them label the large circle "S.T.O.P.," the medium-sized circle "Alternatives to drug use," and the small circles "Why not?" and "Strategies." Have them write the meaning of S.T.O.P. on the back of the large circle. Under the "Alternatives to drug use" tab, have students write alternative activities they can do to be drug free. Have students use the other tabs to list refusal strategies. When they are finished have students share there information with the rest of the class.

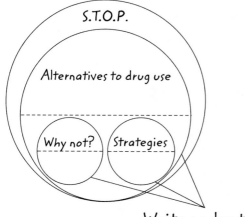

S.T.O.P.

Alternatives to drug use

Why not?   Strategies

Write under tabs.

Student Study Tip

Explain to students that planning a time to study can make study time productive. Finding a time is easy. Have students think about a time during the day that they feel most energized. Coming home and doing homework right away is ideal because things are still fresh on the mind. This doesn't work for all. It is important to plan a time that is not too late in the evening to avoid being tired.

Course 2

FOLDABLES

Personal Health and Consumer Choices

CHAPTER SUMMARY

Daily brushing and flossing, combined with regular dental exams, can keep teeth and gums healthy. Keeping skin and hair clean and protected helps people feel good about themselves. Proper eye and ear care is also important for health. Comparison shopping and reading labels can help consumers choose health products wisely. Both primary care providers and specialists treat patients. Health insurance helps people pay for health care.

CHAPTER PREVIEW

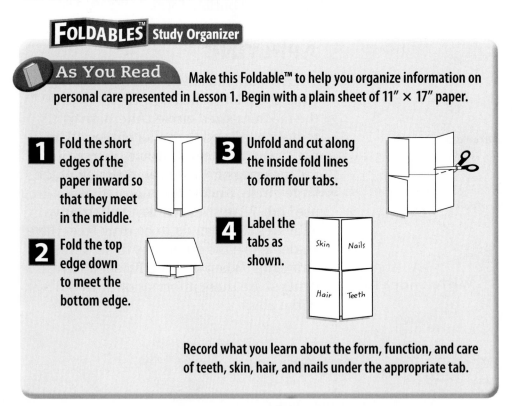

FOLDABLES™ Study Organizer

As You Read Make this Foldable™ to help you organize information on personal care presented in Lesson 1. Begin with a plain sheet of 11″ × 17″ paper.

1 Fold the short edges of the paper inward so that they meet in the middle.

2 Fold the top edge down to meet the bottom edge.

3 Unfold and cut along the inside fold lines to form four tabs.

4 Label the tabs as shown.

Skin   Nails

Hair   Teeth

Record what you learn about the form, function, and care of teeth, skin, hair, and nails under the appropriate tab.

CHAPTER REVIEW

Foldables Follow-Up Activity

After students have completed their Foldable, ask them to write a paragraph describing the manner in which they would prefer to be told by a friend or family member that they need to take better care of their skin, hair, or nails. How might the wrong approach affect their motivation?

Alternative Activities for Chapter 11

IDENTIFYING

Have students create a new Foldable. On the four tabs they should write four of the advertising techniques aimed at teens; they should write the fifth technique on the back of the Foldable. Under each tab and on the back they should write an example of that technique. When they've finished, have them work in small groups to write a public service announcement warning teens about these same techniques. Ask the groups to act out their commercials for the class.

Bandwagon | Beautiful People

Good Times | Status

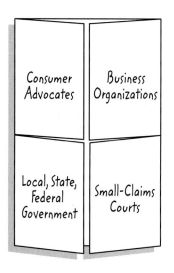

Consumer Advocates | Business Organizations

Local, State, Federal Government | Small-Claims Courts

ANALYZING

Have students create a new Foldable. On the tabs they should write the four types of groups from which a consumer can seek help. Under each tab they should indicate the kinds of help each group provides. When students are finished, ask several students to role-play a store employee and a customer with a problem product. How can the employee help resolve the problem and make the customer feel that he or she is being taken seriously?

Student Study Tip

Some students may have a computer available to them at home but may need to share it with other family members. Encourage them to discuss with their families an "appointment" schedule for using the computer at home for homework. If the computer is located in a social area, they might also want to make sure that their scheduled time is during a quiet period. If no home computer is available, encourage them to find out about scheduling time at the school's computer lab.

Course 2

FOLDABLES

Growing and Changing

CHAPTER SUMMARY

Physical, mental/emotional, and social changes take place during adolescence. Hormones bring about many of these changes. Males and females can practice healthful behaviors to keep their reproductive systems healthy. The human body begins as a single fertilized cell. Parents pass on hereditary traits to their children. Making the most of the teen years requires that teens consider the consequences of possible decisions.

CHAPTER PREVIEW

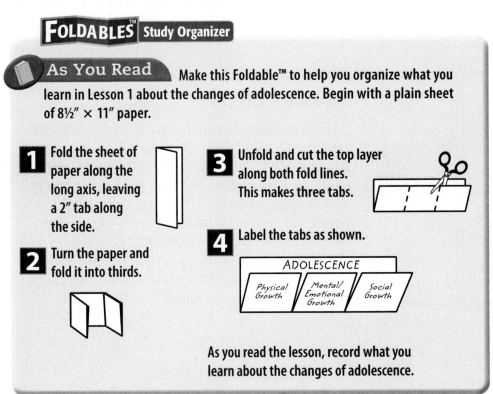

FOLDABLES™ Study Organizer

As You Read Make this Foldable™ to help you organize what you learn in Lesson 1 about the changes of adolescence. Begin with a plain sheet of 8½″ × 11″ paper.

1 Fold the sheet of paper along the long axis, leaving a 2″ tab along the side.

2 Turn the paper and fold it into thirds.

3 Unfold and cut the top layer along both fold lines. This makes three tabs.

4 Label the tabs as shown.

ADOLESCENCE

Physical Growth | Mental/ Emotional Growth | Social Growth

As you read the lesson, record what you learn about the changes of adolescence.

CHAPTER REVIEW

Foldables Follow-Up Activity

Divide the class into small groups. Have students refer to their Foldables to discuss challenges involving the three aspects of health that they or someone they know has overcome. How did the person succeed?

Alternative Activities for Chapter 12

IDENTIFYING

Have students create a new Foldable. Have them label the title tab "Health Concerns" and the other tabs "Male Health," "Female Health," and "Mother and Baby." Under the appropriate tabs students should note the health concerns of males and females and the guidelines for having a healthy baby. If possible, obtain a sonogram image of a developing fetus that you can share with the class. Have them identify the stage of the baby's development.

Health Concerns

| Male Health | Female Health | Mother and Baby |

ILLUSTRATING

Have students create a new Foldable. Have them label the title tab "Stages of the Life Cycle" and the other tabs "Infancy," "Childhood," and "Adolescence/ Adulthood." Under the appropriate tabs students should define terms and take notes on changes that take place during the different stages. When they've finished, have them make collages using drawings, pictures from magazines, and other resources to illustrate these changes.

Stages of the Life Cycle

| Infancy | Childhood | Adolescence/ Adulthood |

Student Study Tip

Discuss with students the importance of learning to listen. Listening means really paying attention to what is being said. Encourage them to take notes, especially during class discussion of important material. For fun, you may want to line up ten students and hand a note to the first student in line, such as "An essay test will be given on Chapter 6 at 5:00 p.m. on May 17." Then ask each student to whisper the message to the next person in line without passing the note along. Compare what the last person heard to what your note said.

Course 2

FOLDABLES

Communicable Diseases

CHAPTER SUMMARY

Communicable diseases include the common cold and the flu. Germs known as pathogens cause communicable diseases. The immune system fights off pathogens. Vaccines can help prevent some diseases. The only sure protection against sexually transmitted diseases is abstinence from sexual activity. People can help stop the spread of pathogens by protecting themselves and others and by developing a healthy lifestyle.

CHAPTER PREVIEW

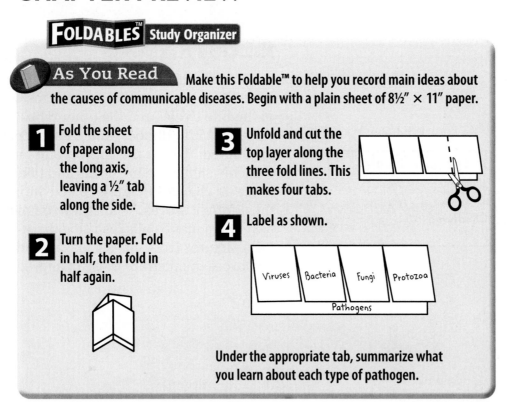

FOLDABLES™ Study Organizer

As You Read Make this Foldable™ to help you record main ideas about the causes of communicable diseases. Begin with a plain sheet of 8½″ × 11″ paper.

1 Fold the sheet of paper along the long axis, leaving a ½″ tab along the side.

2 Turn the paper. Fold in half, then fold in half again.

3 Unfold and cut the top layer along the three fold lines. This makes four tabs.

4 Label as shown.

Viruses Bacteria Fungi Protozoa

Pathogens

Under the appropriate tab, summarize what you learn about each type of pathogen.

CHAPTER REVIEW

Foldables Follow-Up Activity

Have students create a sign listing either the steps in handwashing or ways in which to prevent the spread of disease. Have them decorate the signs with drawings illustrating the pathogens listed on their Foldable and use the signs at home as a reminder to themselves.

Alternative Activities for Chapter 13

SUMMARIZING

Have students create a new Foldable. On the title tab have them write "Major Barriers" and on the other tabs "Tears/ Saliva," "Skin," "Mucous Membranes," and "Stomach Acid." Ask them to summarize what they've learned under each of the tabs. Ask for volunteers to find out about emerging viruses and report to the class. What are they and why are they important?

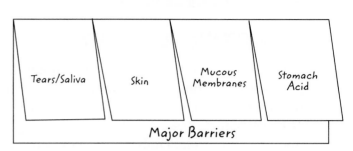

SHARING INFORMATION

On the title tab of a new Foldable, have students write "The Spread of HIV" and on the other tabs "Sexual Activity," "Contaminated Needles," "From Mother to Child," and "Other Modes." Ask them to summarize under each tab what they've learned about the ways that HIV is spread. If students created an e-zine for Chapter 4 and are maintaining it, have them write articles or create graphics for the e-zine about HIV and AIDS. Suggest they add links to other sites that have relevant information.

Student Study Tip

Suggest the following tips to students for taking a test: Quickly skim the entire test and read directions before beginning. Ask the teacher to explain anything you don't understand. Answer the easiest questions first; then you'll know how much time is left for harder questions. When answering an essay question, be sure you understand the directions. What are you being asked to do: explain, compare, discuss, list, or describe? Then be sure you do what is asked. Don't worry if others in the room finish before you do; just focus on your own task. When you finish, check your answers if possible.

Course 2

Noncommunicable Diseases

CHAPTER SUMMARY

Noncommunicable diseases are those that cannot be spread from person to person. They include allergies, asthma, cancer, heart disease, diabetes, and arthritis. Cancer occurs when abnormal cells grow out of control. Heart disease reduces the strength or functioning of the heart and blood vessels. Diabetes prevents the body from converting food into energy. Arthritis is a disease of the joints marked by painful swelling and stiffness.

CHAPTER PREVIEW

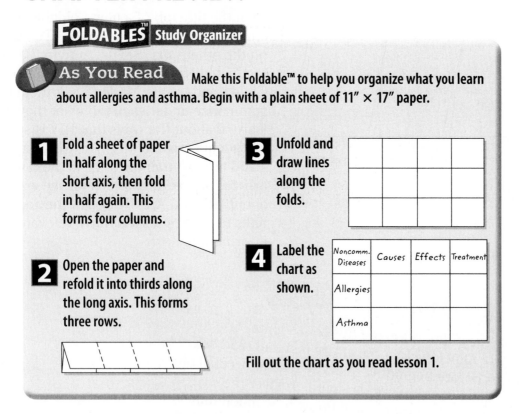

FOLDABLES™ Study Organizer

As You Read Make this Foldable™ to help you organize what you learn about allergies and asthma. Begin with a plain sheet of 11" × 17" paper.

1 Fold a sheet of paper in half along the short axis, then fold in half again. This forms four columns.

2 Open the paper and refold it into thirds along the long axis. This forms three rows.

3 Unfold and draw lines along the folds.

4 Label the chart as shown.

Noncomm. Diseases	Causes	Effects	Treatment
Allergies			
Asthma			

Fill out the chart as you read lesson 1.

CHAPTER REVIEW

Foldables Follow-Up Activity

Ask if any students have known someone with allergies, asthma, or one of the other illnesses discussed in this chapter. What was that person's experience like? What changes in lifestyle did the person make to combat or recover from the illness?

Alternative Activities for Chapter 14

ORGANIZING

Have students make a new Foldable. Have them title the columns "Noncommunicable Diseases," "Causes," "Effects," and "Treatment." Have them title the rows "Cancer" and "Heart Disease." Have them fill out the table with information that they learn in class. Ask the class to create a display for the school illustrating steps teens can take in preventing both diseases.

Noncommunicable Diseases	Causes	Effects	Treatment
Cancer			
Heart Disease			

Arthritis	Cause	Characteristics	Symptoms
Rheumatoid Arthritis			
Osteoarthritis			

COMPARING AND CONTRASTING

Have students create a new Foldable and label the columns "Arthritis," "Cause," "Characteristics," and "Symptoms." Have them label the rows "Rheumatoid Arthritis" and "Osteoarthritis." Ask them to record on the table the information learned in the lesson, noting the diseases' similarities and differences.

Student Study Tip

Write the word *procrastination* on the board. Explain to students that it means putting off doing what needs to be done. Procrastination can be a tough habit to break. One of the first steps in doing so is to recognize that the problem exists. Suggest to students that they make a list of what needs to be done and prioritize it. Which tasks are urgent and need to be handled right away? Which can be done the next day? Caution them to be honest in their evaluation. Then encourage them to handle the tasks in order of priority.

Course 2

FOLDABLES

Personal Safety

CHAPTER SUMMARY

Being safety conscious involves being aware that safety is important and acting in a safe manner. Changing the situation, the unsafe habit, or the unsafe action can break the accident chain. There are many ways to prevent accidents at home, at school, and outdoors. Weather emergencies and natural disasters include tornadoes, hurricanes, blizzards, thunderstorms, floods, and earthquakes. First aid is the immediate care given to someone who is injured or ill until regular medical care arrives. Knowing basic first aid enables people to deal with emergencies.

CHAPTER PREVIEW

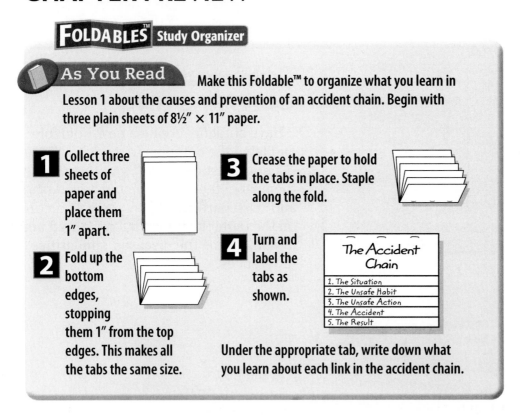

FOLDABLES™ Study Organizer

As You Read — Make this Foldable™ to organize what you learn in Lesson 1 about the causes and prevention of an accident chain. Begin with three plain sheets of 8½″ × 11″ paper.

1 Collect three sheets of paper and place them 1″ apart.

2 Fold up the bottom edges, stopping them 1″ from the top edges. This makes all the tabs the same size.

3 Crease the paper to hold the tabs in place. Staple along the fold.

4 Turn and label the tabs as shown.

The Accident Chain
1. The Situation
2. The Unsafe Habit
3. The Unsafe Action
4. The Accident
5. The Result

Under the appropriate tab, write down what you learn about each link in the accident chain.

CHAPTER REVIEW

Foldables Follow-Up Activity

Divide the class into small groups. Ask students to discuss the information about the accident chain in their Foldable in relation to accidents they've had or nearly had. What was the unsafe habit or action? What could have been done to prevent the accident?

Alternative Activities for Chapter 15

DESCRIBING

Have students create a new Foldable and title it "Causes of Fires." They should label the remaining tabs "Cooking Habits," "Smoking," "Flammable Materials," "Electrical Equipment," and "Vocabulary." Have them describe how fires can start in each category. They should then write and define vocabulary terms under the last tab. On the back of the Foldable they should describe a fire they've witnessed either in person or through the news media. What was its cause?

Causes of Fires

Cooking Habits
Smoking
Flammable Materials
Electrical Equipment
Vocabulary

Weather Emergencies and Natural Disasters

Tornadoes
Hurricanes
Blizzards and Thunderstorms
Floods
Earthquakes

IDENTIFYING

Have students create a new Foldable entitled "Weather Emergencies and Natural Disasters." Have them label the tabs "Tornadoes," "Hurricanes," "Blizzards and Thunderstorms," "Floods," and "Earthquakes." Ask them to identify under each tab the steps to take in the event of each weather emergency or natural disaster. Discuss with students the role of storm trackers in detection and early warning of dangerous storms. If possible show a video of storm trackers at work.

Student Study Tip

When students have difficulty understanding a passage of text, they might want to try asking the Five Ws and H: who, what, when, where, why, and how. If they create a word web, leaving the center circle blank and writing the answers to the Five Ws and H in smaller circles on the outside, they may find the hidden main idea by inference.

Course 2

FOLDABLES

The Environment and Your Health

CHAPTER SUMMARY

Pollution is the presence of dirty or harmful substances in the environment. It includes air pollution, water pollution, and solid waste. Pollution can pose a threat to health. Preventing pollution, managing waste, and conserving water and energy all help protect the environment. By reducing, reusing, and recycling, garbage can be kept out of landfills. Guidelines for home conservation involve heating and cooling, lighting and appliances, cooking, and water use.

CHAPTER PREVIEW

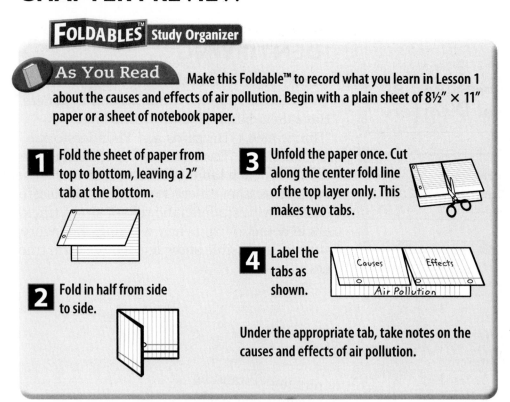

FOLDABLES™ Study Organizer

As You Read Make this Foldable™ to record what you learn in Lesson 1 about the causes and effects of air pollution. Begin with a plain sheet of 8½" × 11" paper or a sheet of notebook paper.

1 Fold the sheet of paper from top to bottom, leaving a 2" tab at the bottom.

2 Fold in half from side to side.

3 Unfold the paper once. Cut along the center fold line of the top layer only. This makes two tabs.

4 Label the tabs as shown.

Causes   Effects
Air Pollution

Under the appropriate tab, take notes on the causes and effects of air pollution.

CHAPTER REVIEW

Foldables Follow-Up Activity

On the back of their Foldable have students identify ways in which air pollution can directly or indirectly affect health. On a separate sheet of paper, have them identify ways in which land and water pollution can affect health.

Alternative Activities for Chapter 16

INTERVIEWING

Ask students to create a new Foldable. Have them label the Foldable "Prevention" and label the tabs "Air" and "Land/Water." Have them record under the tabs what they learn about preventing these two types of pollution. Then have them inter-view an older adult who has lived in the area most of her or his life and ask how the area has changed in terms of pollution. They should write an article about the interview for the school paper or their health e-zine.

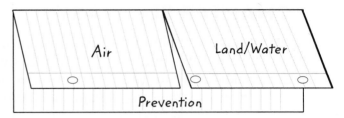

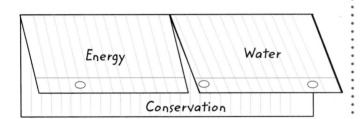

PROBLEM SOLVING

Have students create a new Foldable. Have them label the Foldable "Conservation" and the tabs "Energy" and "Water." Have them take notes under the tabs on what they learn in class about energy and water conservation.

Student Study Tip

Discuss with students how evaluating the result of a test or other assignment can often provide clues to doing better next time. Write the following questions on the board that they can ask themselves: Where did I do my best? Why? Was it because I knew the material well or because I find that type of question easier to answer? What was my biggest difficulty; does any pattern appear? What caused my mistakes? Did I not follow directions or not study enough? Did I run out of time? How can I improve the results next time?

Course 2

FOLDABLES

Understanding Your Health

CHAPTER SUMMARY

Health is a combination of physical, mental/emotional, and social well-being. People can influence their health by the choices and decisions they make. Many changes take place during adolescence. A person's physical, mental/emotional, and social growth are rapid during this time. Teens can take responsibility for their own health by choosing a healthy lifestyle, recognizing and abstaining from risk behaviors, practicing self-control, and staying informed.

CHAPTER PREVIEW

FOLDABLES™ Study Organizer

As You Read Make this Foldable™ to record what you learn about health and wellness in Lesson 1. Begin with a plain sheet of 11" × 17" paper.

1 Fold the short sides of the sheet of paper inward so that they meet in the middle.

2 Draw two circles—one that covers both sides of the Foldable, and one that covers only one side of the Foldable. Label as shown.

3 On the back of each panel of your Foldable, take notes, define terms, and record examples of health and wellness. In the middle section, draw your personal health triangle.

CHAPTER REVIEW

Foldables Follow-Up Activity

Have students divide a sheet of paper into three columns and title the columns "Physical Health," "Mental/Emotional Health," and "Social Health." Give students at least ten minutes to write in each column at least five things they have done recently that have had a positive effect on their health. They can refer to their Foldables for ideas. Then, as a class, discuss the lists and brainstorm other things to add.

Alternative Activities for Chapter 1

COMPARE AND CONTRAST

Have students make a Foldable with "Adolescence" written in the large circle and "Changes" in the smaller circle. Inside the Foldable, have students title the three columns "Physical Changes," "Mental/Emotional Changes," and "Social Changes." Under each word they should list the changes that take place during adolescence.

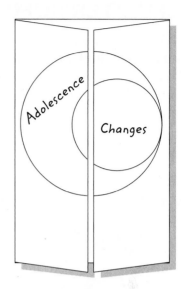

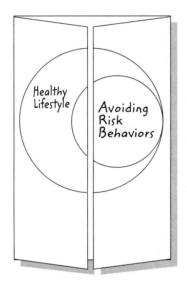

DRAWING CONCLUSIONS

Have students make a Foldable with "Healthy Lifestyle" written in the large circle and "Avoiding Risk Behaviors" written in the smaller circle. Inside the Foldable have students title the three columns "Abstaining," "Taking Responsibility," and "Staying Informed." They should use the space to define each term and take notes.

Student Study Tip

Encourage students to become familiar with their textbooks so they can find things more easily. Point out the different features in each lesson, such as Reading Check and the Health Skills Activity. Go over the Table of Contents with them. Point out the titles of the different units and how chapter topics have been grouped together. Note the lists of activities and features on the following pages. Ask students to explain the difference between a table of contents and an index. What are the purposes and advantages of each?

Course 3

FOLDABLES

Skills for a Healthy Life

CHAPTER SUMMARY

Decision making and goal setting are important health skills. Interpersonal communication involves speaking, listening, and refusal skills. Stress is the body's response to change. Stress-management skills include knowing how to relax, maintaining a positive outlook, being physically active, and managing time. Other important health skills include accessing information, practicing healthful behaviors, and analyzing influences.

CHAPTER PREVIEW

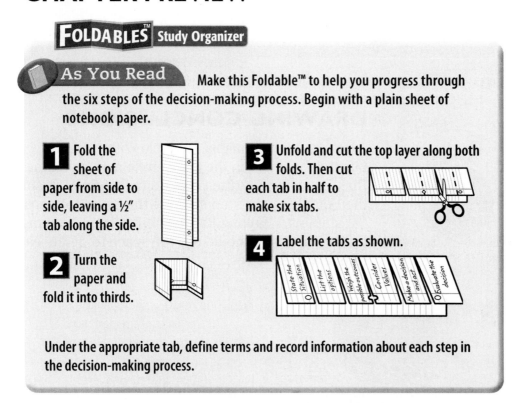

FOLDABLES™ **Study Organizer**

As You Read — Make this Foldable™ to help you progress through the six steps of the decision-making process. Begin with a plain sheet of notebook paper.

1 Fold the sheet of paper from side to side, leaving a ½" tab along the side.

2 Turn the paper and fold it into thirds.

3 Unfold and cut the top layer along both folds. Then cut each tab in half to make six tabs.

4 Label the tabs as shown.

State the Situation | List the options | Weigh the possible outcomes | Consider Values | Make a decision and act | Evaluate the decision

Under the appropriate tab, define terms and record information about each step in the decision-making process.

CHAPTER REVIEW

Foldables Follow-Up Activity

Have students use a separate sheet of paper and, referring to their Foldables, write about a recent decision they've made and how they applied the six decision-making steps. If students can't think of a decision in which all steps were used, ask them to analyze another decision and suggest ways the "missing" steps might have helped.

Alternative Activities for Chapter 2

BRAINSTORMING

Ask students to create a new Foldable, write "The Goal-Setting Process" on the top tab, and write the five goal-setting steps on the remaining tabs. Under the tabs they should take notes and write examples of how the steps are used. Brainstorm with the class reasons that goal setting could have a positive effect on stress.

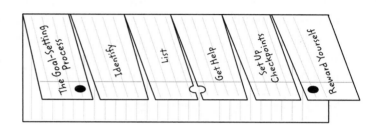

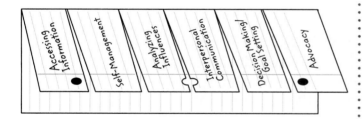

ANALYZING INFLUENCES

Ask students to write the six health skills described in this chapter on the tabs of a new Foldable. Have them take notes under the tabs on what they've learned in this chapter. Then ask students to write a paragraph describing how each of these skills can benefit health.

Student Study Tip

Setting goals is helpful in managing study tasks. Suggest that students create three lists: immediate goals, short-term goals, and long-term goals. Immediate goals often involve things that must be done before other things can be done, such as "Buy paper for printer." Then, next to each goal, they should list things they must accomplish before they can meet the goal. Remind them that long-term goals are not carved in stone. With time and experience their interests and needs may change.

Course 3

FOLDABLES

Mental and Emotional Health

CHAPTER SUMMARY

Personality, self-concept, and self-esteem all affect a person's mental/emotional health. A person can improve mental/emotional health by being motivated, focusing on strengths, understanding and managing feelings, developing a positive attitude, and learning from mistakes. A person can learn to express emotions in healthy ways.

CHAPTER PREVIEW

As You Read Make this Foldable™ to help you organize the main ideas on mental and emotional health in Lesson 1. Begin with a plain sheet of 8½" × 11" paper.

1 Line up one of the short edges of a sheet of paper with one of the long edges to form a triangle. Fold and cut off the leftover rectangle.

3 Cut up one fold line, and stop at the middle. This forms two triangular flaps. Draw an X on one tab, and label the other three as shown.

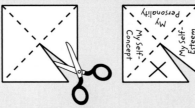

2 Fold the triangle in half, then unfold. The folds will form an X dividing four equal sections.

4 Fold the X flap under the other flap, and glue together to make a three-sided pyramid.

Write the main ideas on mental and emotional health on the back of the appropriate side of the pyramid.

CHAPTER REVIEW

Foldables Follow-Up Activity

Write on the board the following statements based on a quotation from Thomas A. Edison: "I have not failed 10,000 times. I have successfully found 10,000 ways that will not work." Discuss with the class what this quote reveals about Edison's self-concept and attitude based on what they have learned in class.

Alternative Activities for Chapter 3

DESCRIBING

Have students create a new pyramid Foldable with the sides labeled "Identify Emotions," "Express Emotions," and "Understand Emotions." Have them take notes and define terms in the spaces provided. Then ask them to recall a recent emotional experience and, on a separate sheet of paper, write a short story about someone expressing the same emotion in a healthy way.

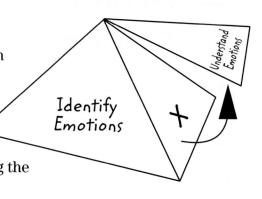

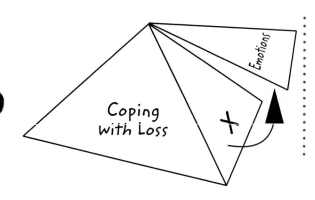

ANALYZING

Ask students to create a new Foldable with the sides labeled "Emotions," "Coping with Loss," and "Managing Stress." Have them record main ideas in the space provided. Discuss with the class the relationship between these three terms.

Student Study Tip

Help students make the best use of Internet resources by showing them how to evaluate a Web site. Write the following questions on the board and suggest that they refer to the questions as they use the Internet: Who owns the Web site? What is the author's expertise? Are any credentials given? Is the site's purpose to entertain, educate, sell, or persuade? When was the information last updated? Does the information seem biased? Is it well written, grammatically correct, and free of spelling errors? This can be a sign of attention paid to quality.

Course 3

FOLDABLES

Mental and Emotional Problems

CHAPTER SUMMARY

The three most common types of mental health problems are anxiety disorders, personality disorders, and mood disorders. People with mental and emotional problems need the help and support of those around them. Depression is a mood disorder that can lasts for weeks or months, the emotional pain can be overwhelming. Life may begin to seem hopeless for some individuals with depression. In extreme cases of hopelessness, there may be thoughts of suicide. It is important to recognize the warning signs of suicide and seek help if you or someone you know is suffering from severe depression. Help for mental and emotional problems include therapy or counseling.

CHAPTER PREVIEW

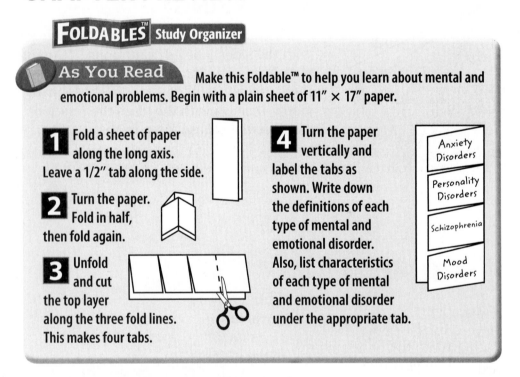

FOLDABLES™ Study Organizer

As You Read Make this Foldable™ to help you learn about mental and emotional problems. Begin with a plain sheet of 11" × 17" paper.

1 Fold a sheet of paper along the long axis. Leave a 1/2" tab along the side.

2 Turn the paper. Fold in half, then fold again.

3 Unfold and cut the top layer along the three fold lines. This makes four tabs.

4 Turn the paper vertically and label the tabs as shown. Write down the definitions of each type of mental and emotional disorder. Also, list characteristics of each type of mental and emotional disorder under the appropriate tab.

Anxiety Disorders

Personality Disorders

Schizophrenia

Mood Disorders

CHAPTER REVIEW

Foldables Follow-Up Activity

Divide the class into small groups. Have the students refer to their Foldables and text to discuss the different types of mental/emotional problems. Have each group develop a public service announcement about one of the mental health problems. Have them include the mental health problem, the symptoms, and where and who to get help from. Have them read or summarize there public service announcement for the class.

Alternative Activities for Chapter 4

ORGANIZING INFORMATION

Have students create a new Foldable and label the tabs "Treatment for mental and emotional problems," "Types of professionals," "Family and friends," and "Other resources." Have them use the textbook and outside resources to organize information and list examples under each tab. Under the "Other" tab, ask students to use the internet or other public resource to list local or national programs that help with mental and emotional problems.

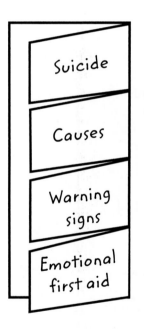

ANALYZING

Have students create a new Foldable to help them understand suicide prevention. Label the flaps of the Foldable "Suicide," "Causes," "Warning signs," and "Emotional first aid." Ask them to take notes as they read and discuss the material in class. When they are finished, divide students into groups and let them discuss and use the text to fill in their Foldable. When students are done, have them write an essay about why emotional first aid is important and how its use can help someone who is having emotional problems. Students can also write their essay into a skit and role-play for the class.

Student Study Tip

Discuss with students the different learning styles. A learning style is a strategy for processing information. The learning styles are visual, auditory, and tactile/kinesthetic. Although, it is common for individuals to use a combination of learning styles there is usually one style that will work best for them. Explain to students, it is a good idea to find their learning style so that they become more efficient when they study.

Course 3

FOLDABLES

Relationships: The Teen Years

CHAPTER SUMMARY

Friendships take on greater importance during the teen years. Most teens also develop an interest in dating. Peers can have a strong influence on teens that can be positive or negative. Effective refusal skills can help teens resist negative peer pressure. Limits are invisible boundaries that can protect a person from risks. Practicing abstinence means not engaging in risk behaviors. The rewards of abstinence are peace of mind, self-respect, time for personal growth, and healthy relationships.

CHAPTER PREVIEW

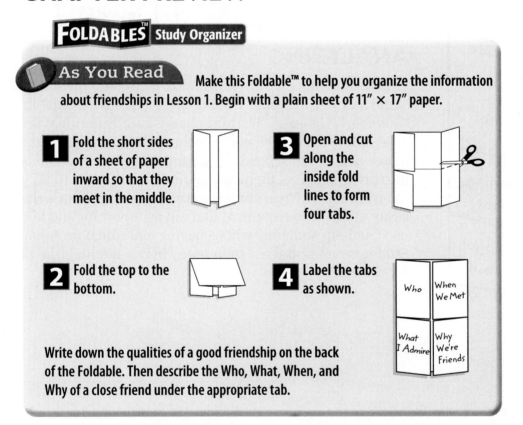

FOLDABLES™ Study Organizer

As You Read   Make this Foldable™ to help you organize the information about friendships in Lesson 1. Begin with a plain sheet of 11" × 17" paper.

1 Fold the short sides of a sheet of paper inward so that they meet in the middle.

3 Open and cut along the inside fold lines to form four tabs.

2 Fold the top to the bottom.

4 Label the tabs as shown.

Who | When We Met
What I Admire | Why We're Friends

Write down the qualities of a good friendship on the back of the Foldable. Then describe the Who, What, When, and Why of a close friend under the appropriate tab.

CHAPTER REVIEW

Foldables Follow-Up Activity

Work with teachers at other schools to establish a collaborative project in which students are paired up as e-mail pen pals to exchange information on health issues. Remind students to use proper "netiquette" (e-mail and chat-room etiquette) when corresponding online.

Alternative Activities for Chapter 5

ANALYZING INFLUENCES

Have students create a new Foldable and write "Peer Pressure," "Positive Peer Pressure," "Negative Peer Pressure," and "Refusal Skills" on the tabs. Under the tabs they should take notes and give examples of each item. Divide the class into small groups to list and discuss methods sometimes used to exert peer pressure, such as attempting to embarrass the person. In what ways can a person's self-concept help the person cope with negative peer pressure?

| Peer Pressure | Positive Peer Pressure |
| Negative Peer Pressure | Refusal Skills |

EVALUATING

Have students create a new Foldable and write "Showing Affection," "Respect for Self and Others," "Avoiding Possible Consequences," and "Rewards of Abstinence" on the tabs. Under the tabs have them take roles on each topic. Then ask students to recall a movie they've seen recently that featured a romantic relationship. Did the relationship involve sexual activity between unmarried people? Discuss whether or not the film showed or implied any negative consequences of this activity. What effect does that have on the truth of the story?

| Showing Affection | Respect for Self and Others |
| Avoiding Possible Consequences | Rewards of Abstinence |

Student Study Tip

Arrange for students to visit the library for a short refresher on how to use its resources. Discuss with them the periodical indexes. If there is an electronic or online version, arrange for the librarian to review its use with the class. Explain how to read entries in the index and show students where back issues of magazines are stored. Ask the librarian to show them how to use the microform reader and how to obtain microfiche or microfilm files.

Course 3

FOLDABLES

Promoting Social Health

CHAPTER SUMMARY

Character is the foundation for all of a person's relationships. Traits of good character are trustworthiness, respect, responsibility, fairness, caring, and citizenship. The family provides support for each of its members. Marriage is a long-term commitment based on good communication, similar values, realistic expectations, and similar interests. Parenting is the process of meeting a child's physical, mental/emotional, and social needs. Teen parenthood can negatively affect nearly every aspect of a teen's life.

CHAPTER PREVIEW

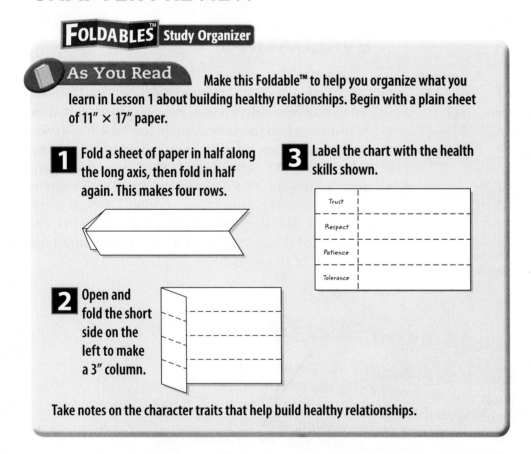

FOLDABLES™ Study Organizer

As You Read Make this Foldable™ to help you organize what you learn in Lesson 1 about building healthy relationships. Begin with a plain sheet of 11″ × 17″ paper.

1 Fold a sheet of paper in half along the long axis, then fold in half again. This makes four rows.

2 Open and fold the short side on the left to make a 3″ column.

3 Label the chart with the health skills shown.

Trust	
Respect	
Patience	
Tolerance	

Take notes on the character traits that help build healthy relationships.

CHAPTER REVIEW

Foldables Follow-Up Activity

Write the following advertisement on the board and ask students to respond in writing. "Help Wanted: A Good Friend. Must have experience. Please write, giving your qualifications."

Alternative Activities for Chapter 6

IDENTIFYING

Have students follow the Foldable directions through Step 2, but only fold the paper one additional time, to make four rows. Have students label the rows "Importance of the Family," "Functions of the Family," "Coping with Family Changes," and "Strengthening Your Family." Have students take notes and write examples in each row. Discuss with students how parents pass along not only hereditary traits but also their dreams for the future. Ask students to identify dreams their parents have had for the family. Ask them to share their own dreams for the future in terms of family. What do they want to pass along to their children?

Importance of the Family		
Functions of the Family		
Coping with Family Changes		
Strengthening Your Family		

Reasons for Marrying		
Factors Affecting Marriage		
Problems in a Marriage		
Teen Marriages		

IDENTIFYING

Have students follow the Foldable directions through Step 2, but only fold the paper one additional time, to make four rows. Label the rows "Reasons for Marrying," "Factors Affecting Marriage," "Problems in a Marriage," and "Teen Marriages." Have students define terms and take notes in each row.

Student Study Tip

Encourage students to improve their listening skills by following these steps:

1. Think about why the person is speaking. What is the speaker's purpose?
2. Signal understanding with eye contact and appropriate body language.
3. If clarification is needed, ask questions.
4. Listen for a tone of voice and body language that reveal feelings and intentions.
5. Listen for signals that mean the speaker has finished.

Course 3

FOLDABLES

Conflict Resolution

CHAPTER SUMMARY

Competition for resources, clashes over values, and disagreements over emotional needs are the main causes of conflicts. Conflicts can worsen when anger, bullying and teasing, group pressure, and alcohol or other drugs are involved. Violence is any act that causes physical or psychological harm to a person or damage to property. Teen violence often involves gangs, weapons, and drugs. Abuse may be physical, emotional, or sexual. Neglect is also a form of abuse. People can help break the cycle of abuse by recognizing it, resisting it, and reporting it.

CHAPTER PREVIEW

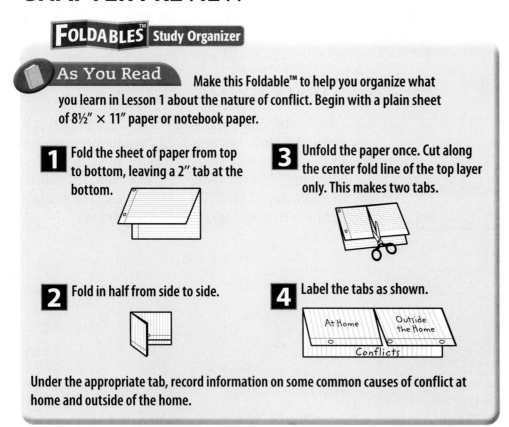

FOLDABLES™ Study Organizer

As You Read Make this Foldable™ to help you organize what you learn in Lesson 1 about the nature of conflict. Begin with a plain sheet of 8½″ × 11″ paper or notebook paper.

1 Fold the sheet of paper from top to bottom, leaving a 2″ tab at the bottom.

2 Fold in half from side to side.

3 Unfold the paper once. Cut along the center fold line of the top layer only. This makes two tabs.

4 Label the tabs as shown.

At Home   Outside the Home

Conflicts

Under the appropriate tab, record information on some common causes of conflict at home and outside of the home.

CHAPTER REVIEW

Foldables Follow-Up Activity

Discuss with students how conflicts in books and movies are used to create interest. Readers and viewers want to know what's going to happen. Does a sense of excitement accompany real-life conflict? What effect might this have on people involved in a conflict?

Alternative Activities for Chapter 7

IDENTIFYING

Have students create a new Foldable and title the tabs "Factors Contributing to Violence" and "Preventing Violence." Have them write examples of factors that contribute to violence under the first tab and the actions that can be taken to prevent violence under the second tab. Ask a civic official to visit the class and discuss ways violence in the community can be prevented.

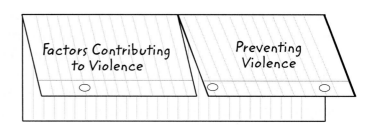

CAUSE AND EFFECT

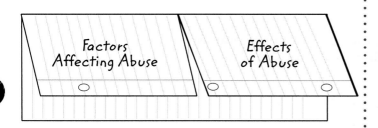

Have students create a new Foldable and title the tabs "Factors Affecting Abuse" and "Effects of Abuse." Have them take notes under the tabs as they study the lesson. Then have students write an essay or short story suggesting ways in which a person's self-concept or self-esteem could help prevent abuse.

Student Study Tip

In working with teams or study groups at school, students may be called upon to teach something to someone else. Discuss with them the best ways to go about it. First, they should approach the subject in a way that they themselves would find interesting. Next, they should organize the information so that it's easy to follow. They should let the learner try different steps on his or her own, while being patient and supportive. They should be sure any criticism is constructive and not personal.

Course 3

FOLDABLES™

Violence Prevention

CHAPTER SUMMARY

Violence can take the form of words and actions. Violence involving teens is on the rise. A teen's environment contributes to their involvement in gangs, drugs, and access to weapons. Teens join gangs because of peer pressure, family problems, and the need to belong to a group. Many schools have a zero tolerance policy, and many take measures to improve safety and reduce violence. Victims of violence suffer injury, loss or death. Some victims are victims of abuse. Abuse can be physical, emotional, or psychological. The cycle of abuse is a pattern of abuse from generation to generation. To break the cycle the victim must get help.

CHAPTER PREVIEW

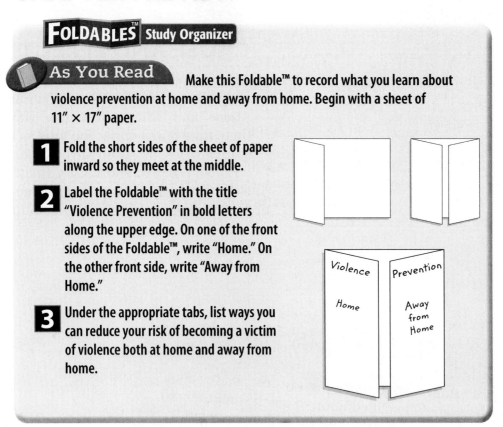

FOLDABLES™ Study Organizer

As You Read   Make this Foldable™ to record what you learn about violence prevention at home and away from home. Begin with a sheet of 11" × 17" paper.

1 Fold the short sides of the sheet of paper inward so they meet at the middle.

2 Label the Foldable™ with the title "Violence Prevention" in bold letters along the upper edge. On one of the front sides of the Foldable™, write "Home." On the other front side, write "Away from Home."

3 Under the appropriate tabs, list ways you can reduce your risk of becoming a victim of violence both at home and away from home.

CHAPTER REVIEW

Foldables Follow-Up Activity

Discuss with students the causes of violence and how it affects its victims. Have students use the information on their Foldable to create a pamphlet for younger students about violence prevention. Ask that they include a community or governmental resource for victims of violence, in their pamphlet. Encourage them to also create a cover for their pamphlet.

Alternative Activities for Chapter 8

ANALYZING

Have students create a new Foldable and use it to analyze the cause and effect of violence. Ask students to label the left front tab "Violence in Our Society," and label the right front tab "Violence in Our School." Ask students to draw an arrow from the left side of the Foldable to the right. Discuss what the arrows means. Does violence in our society spawn violence in our school? Investigate and record information on the cause and effect of violence in our society and violence in our school. Have students share the views and thoughts with the class.

INVESTIGATING

Have students create a new Foldable to help them understand the pros and cons of censoring violence in all forms of media. Ask students to label the left front tab "Pros of Censorship," and label the right front tab "Cons of Censorship." Does violence in the media spawn violence in our society? Ask students to relate how viewing violence affects them personally. Use the internet to investigate and record information on studies conducted on the relationship between violence and the media. Do students agree or disagree with the findings? Have students share their opinions with the class.

Student Study Tip

Discuss with the class the importance of concentration. Concentration requires focus on the task you want to accomplish. There are techniques to stay on task and concentrate. Start by setting a goal for what and how to accomplish your task, for example, # of pages to read and time to accomplish it. If your mind is on other things, write them down and return to them later on. If the task is too large, break it down to smaller task. Study the most difficult material first. After you finish part of the task, summarize or review it.

Course 3

FOLDABLES

Physical Activity and Fitness

CHAPTER SUMMARY

Physical activity includes any movement that uses energy and provides physical, mental/emotional, and social benefits. Exercise develops heart and lung endurance, muscle strength and endurance, and flexibility. Sports conditioning takes time and includes good nutrition. Preventing sports injuries involves behaving safely, using proper equipment, and knowing your limits. Performance-enhancing drugs have no place in a healthy fitness program.

CHAPTER PREVIEW

FOLDABLES™ Study Organizer

 **As You Read** Make this Foldable™ to help you organize the information on physical activity, exercise, and physical fitness presented in Lesson 1. Begin with a plain sheet of 11" × 17" paper.

1 Fold the sheet of paper in half along the short axis, then fold in half again. This forms four columns.

2 Open the paper and refold it in half along the long axis, then fold in half again. This forms four rows.

3 Unfold and draw lines along the folds.

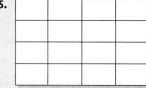

4 Label the chart as shown.

Chapter 9	Definition	Examples	Impact on my life
Physical Activity			
Exercise			
Physical Fitness			

In the appropriate section of the chart, write down definitions and examples of physical activity, exercise, and physical fitness, as well as the impact each has on your daily life.

CHAPTER REVIEW

Foldables Follow-Up Activity

If students created a newsletter or e-zine for Chapter 8, have them add information and articles to it for physical activity and fitness. If they did not create a newsletter or e-zine, divide them into groups and ask each group to prepare an article on fitness or a fitness survey for the school paper.

Alternative Activities for Chapter 9

ORGANIZING DATA

Have students create a new Foldable and title the columns "Heart and Lungs," "Abdomen," "Upper Body," and "Flexibility." Have them label the rows with dates at two-week intervals. Then have them use the Foldable to record test results after each two-week period of improved physical activity.

Heart and Lungs	Abdomen	Upper Body	Flexibility

ANALYZING

Have the class create a new Foldable and label the columns "Staying Fit," "Definitions," "Examples," and "Benefits." Have them label the rows "Sports Activities," "Conditioning," and "Safety." As they read the lesson, they should use the Foldable to define terms, take notes, cite examples, and list benefits. When they've finished, divide the class into groups and ask each group to choose a sports figure, then write a letter to that person asking what that sport has meant to his or her life.

Staying Fit	Definitions	Examples	Benefits
Sports Activities			
Conditioning			
Safety			

Student Study Tip

Students may often be called upon to write formal letters or e-mails for such things as requesting information. Give them these tips:

1. Before you begin, think about what you want to say and to whom you want to say it. If necessary, take notes.
2. Write a rough draft of the letter or e-mail. In the first paragraph, state your purpose in writing. In following paragraphs, go into the necessary details. In the last paragraph, state what, if anything, you would like to have done.
3. Rewrite the letter as needed to make it clear and accurate.
4. Proof the letter for grammar and spelling. Be sure names and addresses are accurate.
5. Make a neat final draft.

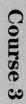

Course 3

FOLDABLES

Nutrition for Health

CHAPTER SUMMARY

Food provides nutrients that promote growth, which is especially important during the teen years. Both external and internal factors influence a person's food choices. The body needs six types of nutrients—carbohydrates, proteins, fats, vitamins, minerals, and water. Hidden fats, cholesterol, added sugars, salt, and caffeine should be eaten in moderation. The Dietary Guidelines for Americans, MyPyramid food guidance system, and the Nutrition Facts panel on food labels can help people make wise food choices. The best snacks are nutrient dense.

CHAPTER PREVIEW

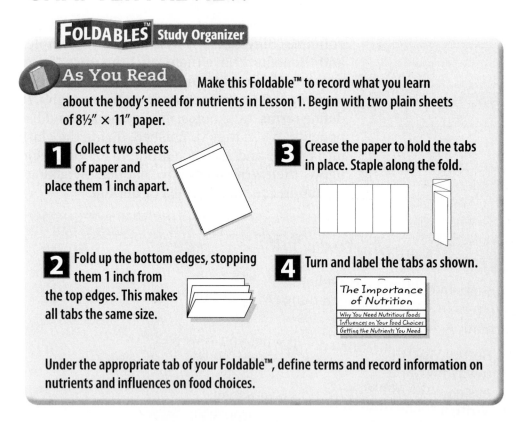

FOLDABLES™ Study Organizer

As You Read Make this Foldable™ to record what you learn about the body's need for nutrients in Lesson 1. Begin with two plain sheets of 8½″ × 11″ paper.

1 Collect two sheets of paper and place them 1 inch apart.

2 Fold up the bottom edges, stopping them 1 inch from the top edges. This makes all tabs the same size.

3 Crease the paper to hold the tabs in place. Staple along the fold.

4 Turn and label the tabs as shown.

The Importance of Nutrition
Why You Need Nutritious Foods
Influences on Your Food Choices
Getting the Nutrients You Need

Under the appropriate tab of your Foldable™, define terms and record information on nutrients and influences on food choices.

CHAPTER REVIEW

Foldables Follow-Up Activity

Have students create an e-zine or printed newsletter about nutrition based on the information in their Foldable and what they've learned so far in class. Suggest they make their publication entertaining and filled with interesting facts, recipes, and hints for a healthier life. If they have e-mail pen pals at other schools, have them send their newsletter or make their e-zine available to those students.

Alternative Activities for Chapter 10

EVALUATING

Have students create a new Foldable and title it "Three Nutrition Guides." Have them label the tabs "The ABCs of Nutrition," "MyPyramid," and "Using Food Labels." Ask them to use their Foldable to record important facts under the appropriate tabs. Ask for volunteers to research foods from different cultures, selecting one meal to evaluate according to the MyPyramid food guidance system.

> ### Three Nutrition Guides
> The ABCs of Nutrition
> MyPyramid
> Using Food Labels

ANALYZING

Have students create a new Foldable and title it "Planning Meals and Snacks." Have them label the tabs "Start with Breakfast," "Plan Meals Wisely," and "Choose Sensible Snacks." Under the tabs they should take notes and cite supporting examples. When they've finished, ask students to research and write a report on recent studies that show that many children in the United States are overweight. At the end of the report they should analyze the information and make recommendations as to what should be done.

> ### Planning Meals and Snacks
> Start with Breakfast
> Plan Meals Wisely
> Choose Sensible Snacks

Student Study Tip

Students are often asked to write reports based on research. Review with them the basics of citing sources. For magazines or newspapers, they must be sure to include the publication's name, date of the edition, title of the article, writer's name, and page number. For books they must include the title, author's name, copyright date, and page numbers for any specific citations. If they plan to use quoted material, they should be sure to copy it accurately and put quotation marks around it.

Course 3

Your Body Image

CHAPTER SUMMARY

Body image is the way a person views his or her body. A person can determine his or her appropriate weight by using the Body Mass Index. Being over- or underweight is unhealthy. To maintain a healthy weight, a person should eat a nutritious diet and stay active. Eating disorders are extreme and damaging eating behaviors that can lead to sickness and even death. They include anorexia nervosa, bulimia, and binge eating disorder. People with eating disorders should seek help.

CHAPTER PREVIEW

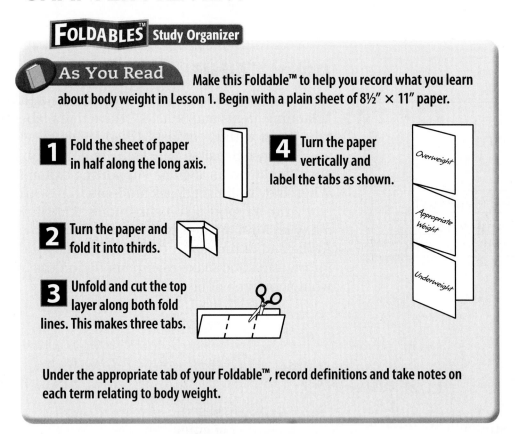

FOLDABLES™ Study Organizer

As You Read Make this Foldable™ to help you record what you learn about body weight in Lesson 1. Begin with a plain sheet of 8½″ × 11″ paper.

1 Fold the sheet of paper in half along the long axis.

2 Turn the paper and fold it into thirds.

3 Unfold and cut the top layer along both fold lines. This makes three tabs.

4 Turn the paper vertically and label the tabs as shown.

Overweight

Appropriate Weight

Underweight

Under the appropriate tab of your Foldable™, record definitions and take notes on each term relating to body weight.

CHAPTER REVIEW

Foldables Follow-Up Activity

Ask students to obtain from the library a book or videotape on weight loss and evaluate the program based on what they've learned in class.

Alternative Activities for Chapter 11

RESEARCHING

Have students create a new Foldable with these labels: "Adjusting Calorie Intake," "Recognizing Risks," and "Weight-Management Tips." Ask them to take notes as they read and discuss the material in class. When they've finished, ask them to research and write a report on foods that ostensibly help people control weight, such as diet colas. Do they help or not? Are there side effects? Direct them toward such resources as the Center for Science in the Public Interest.

APPLYING KNOWLEDGE

Have students create a new Foldable with "Anorexia," "Bulimia," and "Binge Eating Disorder" written on the tabs. Under each tab they should write a description of that type of disorder. When they've finished, ask them to imagine they are advice columnists for a teen magazine. They've just received a letter from a teen whose boyfriend has told her she's overweight; now she's looking for a diet that will help her lose weight fast so she can keep her boyfriend. Have them answer the letter, giving her advice based on what they've learned in class.

Student Study Tip

Ask students if they've ever asked someone, "What's your point?" What they were looking for was the main idea the person was trying to get across. The main idea is the most important point. Encourage students to look for the main ideas in paragraphs as they read. They can usually find the main idea by first skimming the paragraph for a sentence that seems to tell what the paragraph is about. Does the rest of the paragraph give details about this topic? If so, they've found the main idea.

Course 3

Alcohol

CHAPTER SUMMARY

Alcohol, like other depressant drugs, slows down the function of the brain and other parts of the nervous system. Several factors influence its effect on a person. Alcohol can interfere with a teen's growth processes. Alcohol is also a threat to society. It can lead to injuries and addiction. Many support groups are available for alcoholics and their families. More and more young people are choosing not to drink. They have seen through media messages and have found alternatives to drinking alcohol.

CHAPTER PREVIEW

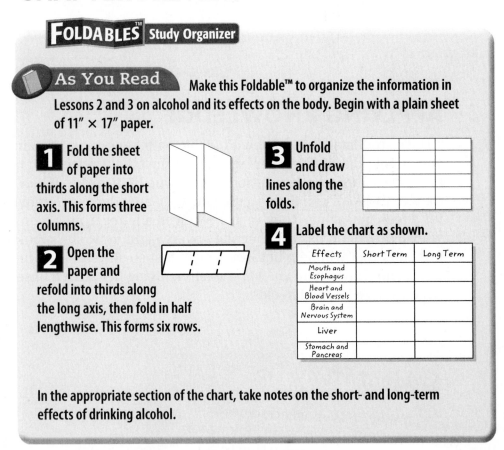

FOLDABLES™ Study Organizer

As You Read Make this Foldable™ to organize the information in Lessons 2 and 3 on alcohol and its effects on the body. Begin with a plain sheet of 11″ × 17″ paper.

1 Fold the sheet of paper into thirds along the short axis. This forms three columns.

2 Open the paper and refold into thirds along the long axis, then fold in half lengthwise. This forms six rows.

3 Unfold and draw lines along the folds.

4 Label the chart as shown.

Effects	Short Term	Long Term
Mouth and Esophagus		
Heart and Blood Vessels		
Brain and Nervous System		
Liver		
Stomach and Pancreas		

In the appropriate section of the chart, take notes on the short- and long-term effects of drinking alcohol.

CHAPTER REVIEW

Foldables Follow-Up Activity

Write the following on the board: "The sale of alcohol should/should not be made illegal in the U.S." Then ask students to take a position on the topic and write a paragraph explaining their reasons.

Alternative Activities for Chapter 12

INTERVIEWING

Have students create a new Foldable and label the columns "Vocabulary Term," "Definition," and "Used in a Sentence." Have them write the following vocabulary terms in the first column: "Alcohol," "Blood Alcohol Content," "Intoxicated," "Binge Drinking," and "Fetal Alcohol Syndrome." Then have them fill in the rest of the table. If appropriate, arrange for the class to have an online "chat" with an expert on alcoholism. Ask students to prepare questions for the expert in advance based on what they've learned in this chapter.

Vocabulary Term	Definition	Used in a Sentence
Alcohol		
Blood Alcohol Content		
Intoxicated		
Binge Drinking		
Fetal Alcohol Syndrome		

COMPARING

Have students create a new Foldable and label the columns "Reasons to Drink," "The Real Facts," and "Better Alternatives." Have them write in the rows under the first column "It looks grown up," "I'll forget my problems," "It will help me relax," "My friends pressure me," and "It looks like fun." Then have them fill out the table with information from the chapter and their own suggestions for alternative activities. If appropriate, have students visit the Web sites of various resources that offer help for alcohol addiction, such as the Betty Ford Center, to discover what services are available for patients and families. Then ask students to create a table in which they compare the information.

Reasons to Drink	The Real Facts	Better Alternatives
It looks grown up		
I'll forget my problems		
It will help me relax		
My friends pressure me		
It looks like fun		

Student Study Tip

All students can benefit from a few test-taking strategies. Write the following strategies on the board:

1. Be sure you have all the materials with you that you will need.
2. Arrive early so that you have time to gather your thoughts and won't be rushed.
3. Listen carefully to instructions.
4. Budget your time wisely.
5. Answer easy questions first.
6. Change answers only if you are sure they are wrong. Your first instincts are probably correct.

Course 3

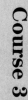

FOLDABLES

Tobacco

CHAPTER SUMMARY

Cigarettes, cigars and pipes, smokeless tobacco, and specialty cigarettes are all forms of tobacco. Tobacco contains harmful substances that change the body's chemistry: nicotine, tar, and carbon monoxide. Addiction to tobacco involves both physical and psychological dependence and results in high costs to society. Teens may start to use tobacco because of internal and external influences. The best way to lead a tobacco-free life is to never start using it.

CHAPTER PREVIEW

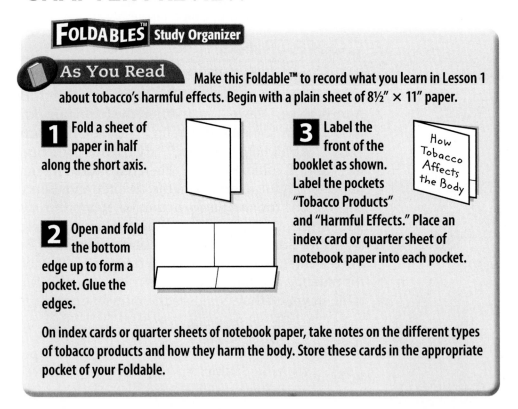

FOLDABLES™ Study Organizer

As You Read Make this Foldable™ to record what you learn in Lesson 1 about tobacco's harmful effects. Begin with a plain sheet of 8½″ × 11″ paper.

1 Fold a sheet of paper in half along the short axis.

2 Open and fold the bottom edge up to form a pocket. Glue the edges.

3 Label the front of the booklet as shown. Label the pockets "Tobacco Products" and "Harmful Effects." Place an index card or quarter sheet of notebook paper into each pocket.

How Tobacco Affects the Body

On index cards or quarter sheets of notebook paper, take notes on the different types of tobacco products and how they harm the body. Store these cards in the appropriate pocket of your Foldable.

CHAPTER REVIEW

Foldables Follow-Up Activity

Teens may try smoking because it looks "cool." The smoker seems to have a certain grown-up detachment that makes him or her appear in control. Discuss this idea with the class. Ask them what mental/emotional factors are at work. Why do people feel a need to be in control?

Alternative Activities for Chapter 13

RESEARCHING

Ask students to create a new Foldable titled "Tobacco and Society." Have them label the pockets "Tobacco Addiction" and "Costs to Society." Direct them to take notes on each topic on index cards or quarter sheets of notebook paper and store them in the appropriate pocket of the Foldable.

ANALYZING INFLUENCES

Have students create a new Foldable titled "Staying Tobacco Free." Have them label the pockets "Why Some Teens Start" and "How Not to Start." Ask them to take notes on each topic on index cards or quarter sheets of notebook paper and store them in the appropriate pocket of the Foldable.

Student Study Tip

Some students may feel anxious when taking a quiz or being asked to respond in class because they don't remember information well. Write the following tips on the board for remembering information:

1. Connect the new information to what you already know.
2. Repeat the information by reciting it or writing it down.
3. Use memory tricks, such as short poems or songs that give clues, such as "I before E except after C."
4. When applicable, form a mental picture that is related to the information.

Course 3

FOLDABLES

Drugs

CHAPTER SUMMARY

Drugs are substances other than food that change the structure or functioning of the body or mind. Medicines are drugs used to treat or prevent diseases and other conditions. People can harm themselves by misusing or abusing drugs. Commonly abused drugs include narcotics, stimulants, and depressants. Illegal drugs include street drugs, marijuana, hallucinogens, inhalants, club drugs, and anabolic steroids. Using them can have harmful consequences. Avoiding drugs and staying drug free have a positive effect on a person's health. Help is available for people who have difficulty recovering from addiction.

CHAPTER PREVIEW

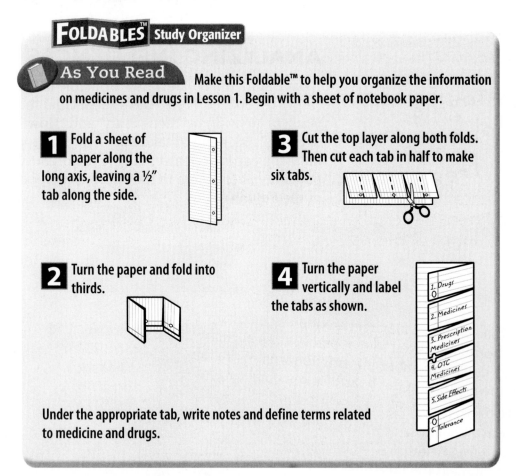

FOLDABLES™ Study Organizer

As You Read Make this Foldable™ to help you organize the information on medicines and drugs in Lesson 1. Begin with a sheet of notebook paper.

1 Fold a sheet of paper along the long axis, leaving a ½" tab along the side.

2 Turn the paper and fold into thirds.

3 Cut the top layer along both folds. Then cut each tab in half to make six tabs.

4 Turn the paper vertically and label the tabs as shown.

1. Drugs
2. Medicines
3. Prescription Medicines
4. OTC Medicines
5. Side Effects
6. Tolerance

Under the appropriate tab, write notes and define terms related to medicine and drugs.

CHAPTER REVIEW

Foldables Follow-Up Activity

If appropriate, acquaint students with online medical sites such as WebMD or the Merck Manual. Ask them to analyze the information available on prescription drugs. Does it seem reliable? Does the site accept advertising? If so, how might that have either a positive or negative influence on the site?

Alternative Activities for Chapter 14

ANALYZING

Have students create a new Foldable with the following terms: "Narcotics," "Marijuana," "Stimulants," "Depressants," "Hallucinogens," and "Inhalants." Have them define each term under the tab and note any important information. After previewing it yourself for appropriateness, ask students to watch a film on recovering from drug abuse. Ask them to determine what mental/emotional health factors played a part in the main character's addiction.

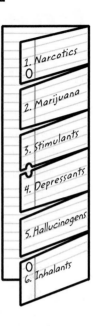

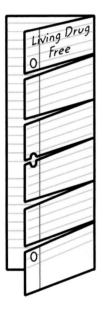

DECISION MAKING

Ask students to create a new Foldable. On the top tab they should write "Living Drug Free." For the remaining tabs, have them draw from the text and their own experiences to write ways in which they can enjoy life without using drugs. Under the tabs they should then write examples of each. Ask the school counselor to speak to the class about resources at the school and in the community for helping teens recover from addiction.

Student Study Tip

Acquaint students with the SQ3R method for improving reading comprehension and memory. S stands for *survey*, which means to preview the material by looking at such things as the title, headings, and illustrations. Q stands for *questions*. Students should read the lesson and chapter review to know what information to look for. 3R stands for *read, recite,* and *review.* They should read the material, recite the answers to the questions, and review the answers again later to keep the information fresh in their minds.

Course 3

FOLDABLES

Personal Care and Consumer Choices

CHAPTER SUMMARY

Having healthy skin means keeping it clean, protecting it from the sun, and treating it gently. Hair and nails must also be kept clean. To maintain healthy teeth, a person must brush and floss regularly, choose snacks wisely, protect teeth during contact sports, and get regular check-ups. Maintaining healthy eyes means protecting them from bright light and injury. Ears are involved in balance as well as hearing and must be protected from the cold and loud noises. Staying healthy also includes being a skillful health consumer. Health services and public health work together in maintaining or improving the health of society.

CHAPTER PREVIEW

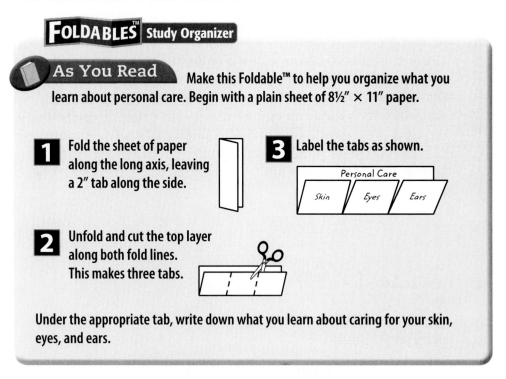

FOLDABLES™ Study Organizer

As You Read Make this Foldable™ to help you organize what you learn about personal care. Begin with a plain sheet of 8½" × 11" paper.

1 Fold the sheet of paper along the long axis, leaving a 2" tab along the side.

3 Label the tabs as shown.

Personal Care

Skin   Eyes   Ears

2 Unfold and cut the top layer along both fold lines. This makes three tabs.

Under the appropriate tab, write down what you learn about caring for your skin, eyes, and ears.

CHAPTER REVIEW

Foldables Follow-Up Activity

"Consumer Beware" is a common statement from consumer advocates about claims and hype made by advertisers of their product. Have students research and write on advertising claims made by cosmetics, and other consumer health products. Ask volunteers to read or give a brief summary of their paper to the class.

Alternative Activities for Chapter 15

ANALYZING

Have students create a new Foldable. Have them title the Foldable "Consumer Choices." Label the tabs "Influences," "Product claims," and "Warranty." Bring or have students bring ads from newspapers or magazines of consumer products. Have students work in groups and examine the information from the ad. Instruct students to state information relevant to their ad and their own consumer viewpoints.

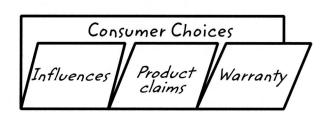

COMPARE AND CONTRAST

Have students create a new Foldable. Have them title the Foldable "Health Care." Label tabs "Health Care System," "Preventive Care" and "Public Health." Using the textbook, have students collect information about the tab topics. Instruct students to think about the relationship and difference of each area of health care.

Student Study Tip

Help students make the best out of their study time. Explain to students that minimizing the distractions in their study environment can help them get work done. They should begin by examining their study area. For example, lighting, environmental noises, good ventilation, air temperature, space, etc. They should adjust these distractions to maximize their comfort.

Course 3

FOLDABLES

Your Body Systems

CHAPTER SUMMARY

The skeletal system provides a framework for the body and, along with the muscular system, helps the body move. The circulatory system carries essential materials to body cells and removes wastes. The respiratory system takes in air, providing the body with oxygen, and removes carbon dioxide. The nervous system helps control other body functions. The digestive system takes in nutrients from food, and the excretory system eliminates wastes. Chemicals produced by the endocrine system activate and control many body processes. The reproductive system enables humans to reproduce.

CHAPTER PREVIEW

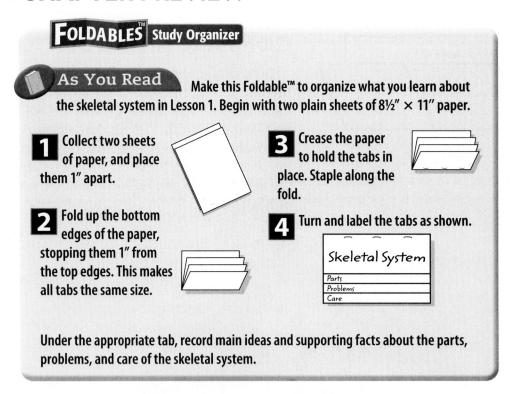

FOLDABLES™ Study Organizer

As You Read Make this Foldable™ to organize what you learn about the skeletal system in Lesson 1. Begin with two plain sheets of 8½″ × 11″ paper.

1 Collect two sheets of paper, and place them 1″ apart.

2 Fold up the bottom edges of the paper, stopping them 1″ from the top edges. This makes all tabs the same size.

3 Crease the paper to hold the tabs in place. Staple along the fold.

4 Turn and label the tabs as shown.

Skeletal System
Parts
Problems
Care

Under the appropriate tab, record main ideas and supporting facts about the parts, problems, and care of the skeletal system.

CHAPTER REVIEW

Foldables Follow-Up Activity

Ask students to interview an older person about skeletal system problems and care. What steps is the person taking to ensure skeletal health? Has the person experienced any problems so far? Obtain an X ray or scan of bones that shows a break, arthritis, or osteoporosis and show it to the class.

Alternative Activities for Chapter 16

ENRICHMENT

Have students create two new Foldables, one titled "Your Circulatory System" and the other titled "Your Respiratory System." Have them label the tabs "Parts of the System," "Problems of the System," and "Care of the System" and record important information under the tabs. If possible, invite a health care professional to demonstrate a stress test to the class and explain what the test reveals. Have students prepare questions for the speaker in advance based on what they've learned in class.

Your
Circulatory System

Parts of the System
Problems of the System
Care of the System

Your
Digestive System

Parts of the System
Problems of the System
Care of the System

PROBLEM SOLVING

Have students create a new Foldable for each of the remaining body systems. Have them label the tabs "Parts of the System," "Problems of the System," and "Care of the System." Divide the class into teams and ask each team to research a problem of one of the systems—their choice. They should focus on any preventive steps that might avert the problem and write a short report on their findings.

Student Study Tip

Students will find written reports easier to complete successfully if they make sure they are clear about the subject, the format, the writing style, the required number of pages, and the date the report is due. Writing a topic statement describing what the report will be about is helpful in establishing their focus. Encourage them to do as many drafts as necessary to ensure that the report is clear and that grammar and spelling are correct. If possible, they should ask someone else to read the report and note any errors or ideas that need clarifying.

Course 3

FOLDABLES

Growth and Development

CHAPTER SUMMARY

A human being begins as a single fertilized egg cell. As the fetus grows and develops, the mother's body provides nutrients. Heredity is the passing of traits from parents to children, and it can influence health. Birth defects are abnormalities in the child that are present at birth. Stages of the life cycle include infancy, childhood, adolescence, and adulthood.

CHAPTER PREVIEW

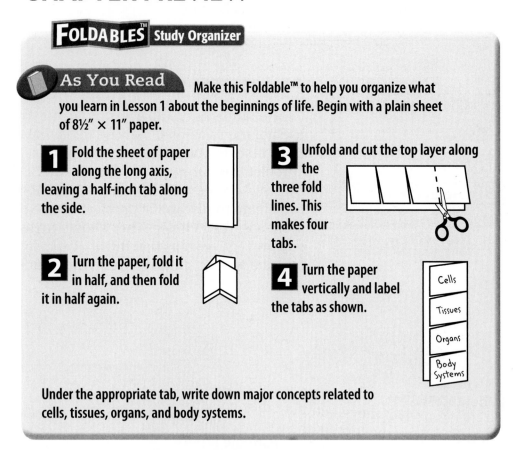

FOLDABLES™ Study Organizer

As You Read Make this Foldable™ to help you organize what you learn in Lesson 1 about the beginnings of life. Begin with a plain sheet of 8½″ × 11″ paper.

1 Fold the sheet of paper along the long axis, leaving a half-inch tab along the side.

2 Turn the paper, fold it in half, and then fold it in half again.

3 Unfold and cut the top layer along the three fold lines. This makes four tabs.

4 Turn the paper vertically and label the tabs as shown.

Cells

Tissues

Organs

Body Systems

Under the appropriate tab, write down major concepts related to cells, tissues, organs, and body systems.

CHAPTER REVIEW

Foldables Follow-Up Activity

Ask if any students have taken classes in babysitting. If so, ask them to share what they have learned about caring for babies with the class. How has their babysitting experience changed or expanded their thinking about having children? If possible, obtain a sonogram of a developing fetus and share it with the class.

Alternative Activities for Chapter 17

SYNTHESIZING

Have students create a new Foldable and label the tabs "Infancy," "Childhood," "Adolescence," and "Adulthood." Have them organize information, define terms, and list examples under each tab. Divide the class into small groups. Ask each group to create a photo essay or multimedia presentation titled "Life Is Change." Encourage them to be creative.

Infancy

Childhood

Adolescence

Adulthood

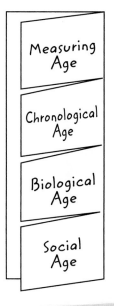

Measuring Age

Chronological Age

Biological Age

Social Age

ANALYZING

Have students create a new Foldable and label the tabs "Measuring Age," "Chronological Age," "Biological Age," and "Social Age." Ask them to define terms and record their impressions under the tabs. Ask students to research how old age is regarded in other cultures, such as that of China. Have them suggest ways in which older Americans can remain a vital part of their communities.

Student Study Tip

Help students streamline their note-taking. It will increase their speed and allow them to record more information in the same amount of time. Suggest the following:

1. Abbreviate and leave the periods off the abbreviations.
2. Use word beginnings, such as *intro* for *introduction.*
3. Use symbols, such as × for *times.*
4. Eliminate vowels, articles, and helper verbs, to create notes such as *Bk wrttn 1890.*
5. Make up a personal version of shorthand.

Course 3

Communicable Diseases

CHAPTER SUMMARY

Organisms called pathogens, which include bacteria and viruses, are the cause of communicable diseases. Illness occurs when pathogens enter the body. The immune system is the main line of defense against pathogens. Vaccination can help defend people against some diseases. Common communicable diseases include the common cold, influenza, strep throat, hepatitis, and mononucleosis. Sexually transmitted diseases (STDs) are infections transmitted through sexual contact. The only sure protection against STDs is abstinence. AIDS is a deadly STD that interferes with the body's natural ability to fight infection. It is caused by the HIV virus.

CHAPTER PREVIEW

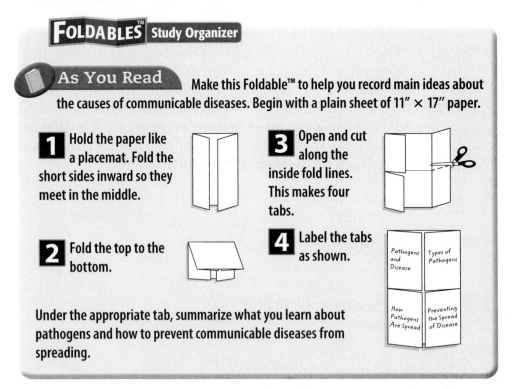

FOLDABLES™ Study Organizer

As You Read Make this Foldable™ to help you record main ideas about the causes of communicable diseases. Begin with a plain sheet of 11″ × 17″ paper.

1 Hold the paper like a placemat. Fold the short sides inward so they meet in the middle.

2 Fold the top to the bottom.

3 Open and cut along the inside fold lines. This makes four tabs.

4 Label the tabs as shown.

Pathogens and Disease | Types of Pathogens
How Pathogens Are Spread | Preventing the Spread of Disease

Under the appropriate tab, summarize what you learn about pathogens and how to prevent communicable diseases from spreading.

CHAPTER REVIEW

Foldables Follow-Up Activity

If students created a newsletter or e-zine for an earlier activity, ask them to add material to it about preventing the spread of disease. If they have not created a newsletter or e-zine, have them create clever signs encouraging handwashing to be posted in school washrooms and the cafeteria.

Alternative Activities for Chapter 18

INVESTIGATING

Have students create a new Foldable and label the tabs "Influenza," "Strep Throat," "Hepatitis," and "Mononucleosis." Have them define terms and describe symptoms for each of diseases under the appropriate tabs. Ask students to check NASA's Web site for information about steps taken when an astronaut becomes ill on the International Space Station.

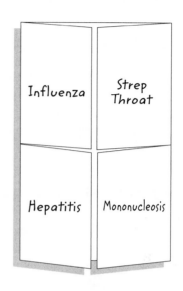

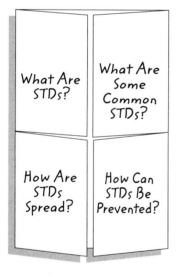

ANALYZING

Have students create a new Foldable and write on the tabs: "What Are STDs?" "What Are Some Common STDs?" "How Are STDs Spread?" "How Can STDs Be Prevented?" Have them write answers to the questions under the tabs. Discuss with them how emerging pathogens, such as the West Nile virus, are becoming more common as humans encroach on the pathogens' habitats.

Student Study Tip

Some students may need help when they try to summarize a passage. Suggest that they first make a list of the main ideas. Next, they should identify the important details by asking who, what, when, where, why, and how. They should then write the summary in their own words. Remind them that a summary is shorter than the original material. It sums up what has been said.

Course 3

FOLDABLES

Noncommunicable Diseases

CHAPTER SUMMARY

Noncommunicable diseases result from factors present at birth, from lifestyle choices, from environmental hazards, or from unknown factors. Allergies, asthma, cancer, heart disease, diabetes, and arthritis are all noncommunicable diseases. There are many actions people can take to reduce the risk of developing a noncommunicable disease.

CHAPTER PREVIEW

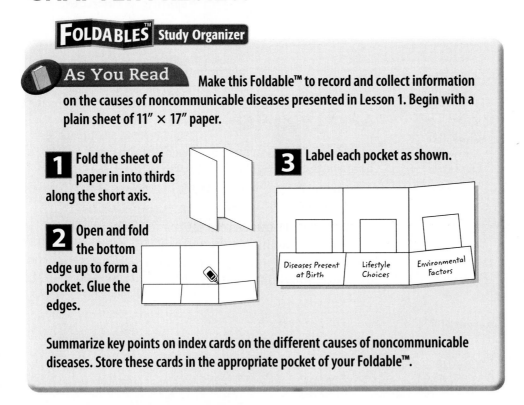

FOLDABLES™ Study Organizer

As You Read Make this Foldable™ to record and collect information on the causes of noncommunicable diseases presented in Lesson 1. Begin with a plain sheet of 11″ × 17″ paper.

1 Fold the sheet of paper in into thirds along the short axis.

2 Open and fold the bottom edge up to form a pocket. Glue the edges.

3 Label each pocket as shown.

Diseases Present at Birth

Lifestyle Choices

Environmental Factors

Summarize key points on index cards on the different causes of noncommunicable diseases. Store these cards in the appropriate pocket of your Foldable™.

CHAPTER REVIEW

Foldables Follow-Up Activity

Have students research mind/ body, or holistic, medicine. Divide them into smaller groups for panel discussions on the value of mind/body medicine in preventing or curing disease.

Alternative Activities for Chapter 19

CAUSES AND EFFECTS

Have students make a new Foldable and label the pockets "Types of Cancer," "Diagnosis and Treatment of Cancer," and "Preventing Cancer." Ask them to record information and define terms on index cards or quarter sheets of notebook paper. Encourage students to participate in a fundraising event, such as the Race for the Cure, or to contact a local support group and organize their own community event.

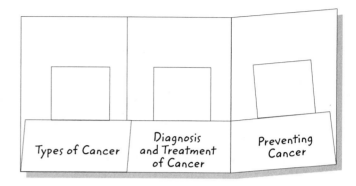

ANALYZING

Have students make a new Foldable and label the pockets "Types of Heart Disease," "Treating Heart and Circulatory Problems," and "Preventing Heart Disease." Have them investigate studies being conducted by pharmaceutical companies on new treatments. What protocols are used and how are volunteers chosen to participate?

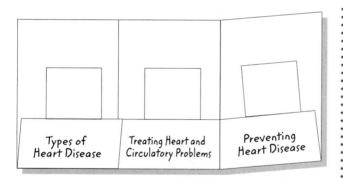

Student Study Tip

Some students may have difficulty answering essay questions if they do not grasp what is being asked for. Review with them the meanings of common verbs used in the instructions for essay questions to be sure they know how to respond. Examples might include: *list, outline, define, criticize, describe, compare, contrast, discuss, summarize.*

Course 3

Safety and Emergencies

CHAPTER SUMMARY

An accident is any event that was not intended to happen. Changing the situation, the unsafe habit, or the unsafe action can break the accident chain. There are many ways to prevent accidents at home, at school, and outdoors. People can protect themselves from dangerous weather and natural disasters by staying alert and knowing what to do if disaster strikes. Firstaid is the immediate care given to someone who is injured or ill until regular medical care arrives. Knowing basic first-aid enables people to cope with emergencies.

CHAPTER PREVIEW

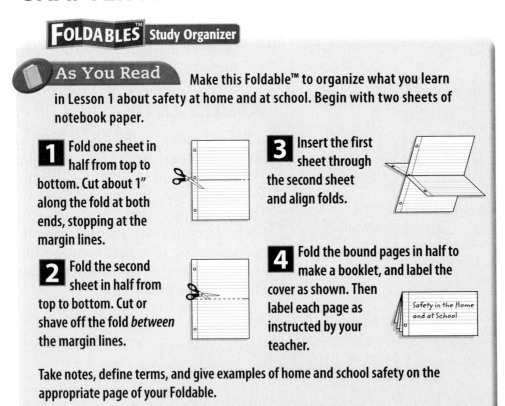

FOLDABLES™ Study Organizer

As You Read Make this Foldable™ to organize what you learn in Lesson 1 about safety at home and at school. Begin with two sheets of notebook paper.

1 Fold one sheet in half from top to bottom. Cut about 1" along the fold at both ends, stopping at the margin lines.

2 Fold the second sheet in half from top to bottom. Cut or shave off the fold *between* the margin lines.

3 Insert the first sheet through the second sheet and align folds.

4 Fold the bound pages in half to make a booklet, and label the cover as shown. Then label each page as instructed by your teacher.

Safety in the Home and at School

Take notes, define terms, and give examples of home and school safety on the appropriate page of your Foldable.

CHAPTER REVIEW

Foldables Follow-Up Activity

Invite the school nurse or another health care professional to demonstrate basic first-aid or other emergency procedures to the class. Have students prepare questions in advance based on what they've learned in class.

Alternative Activities for Chapter 20

IDENTIFYING

Have students create a new Foldable and title it "Hazardous Weather and Natural Disasters." Have them label the inside pages "Tornadoes," "Hurricanes," "Blizzards," "Floods," "Earthquakes," and "Vocabulary" and take notes on each page. Obtain a video about weather emergencies to show the class. Discuss the risks that people take when deciding to videotape dangerous events.

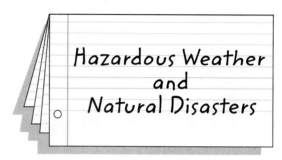

APPLYING KNOWLEDGE

Have students create a new Foldable and title it "First Aid." Have them label the inside pages "What Is First Aid?," "The First Steps," "Common Emergencies," "Life-Threatening Emergencies," "The ABCs of CPR," and "CPR for Adults." Have students use the Foldable to take notes, define terms, and give examples. Discuss with the class the correct way to rescue someone undergoing electric shock who is still "attached" to the circuit. Explain how a circuit works and that they must never touch the person directly but use an insulator to disengage him or her from the circuit.

Student Study Tip

Some students may have trouble reading or taking tests because of limited vocabulary. Suggest that they improve their vocabulary by reading more. To ensure motivation, have them select subjects they are especially interested in. Encourage them to pay attention to new words to learn their meaning rather than skipping over them. Suggest that they keep vocabulary notebooks and have a pocket dictionary on hand.

Course 3

FOLDABLES

Environmental Health

CHAPTER SUMMARY

The health of the environment affects the health of human beings. Pollution includes any dirty or harmful substance in the environment and affects air, water, and land. Most forms of pollution are the result of human activity. The three Rs—reduce, reuse, and recycle—are practices that can help control pollution. They also save resources. People can help the environment by being advocates on its behalf.

CHAPTER PREVIEW

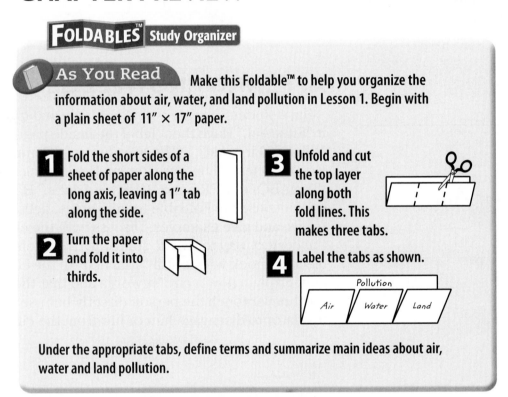

FOLDABLES™ Study Organizer

As You Read Make this Foldable™ to help you organize the information about air, water, and land pollution in Lesson 1. Begin with a plain sheet of 11″ × 17″ paper.

1 Fold the short sides of a sheet of paper along the long axis, leaving a 1″ tab along the side.

2 Turn the paper and fold it into thirds.

3 Unfold and cut the top layer along both fold lines. This makes three tabs.

4 Label the tabs as shown.

Pollution
Air   Water   Land

Under the appropriate tabs, define terms and summarize main ideas about air, water and land pollution.

CHAPTER REVIEW

Foldables Follow-Up Activity

Divide the class into small groups and have them investigate alternative sources of energy that might have fewer negative impacts on the environment. How would each affect air, water, and land?

Alternative Activities for Chapter 21

IDENTIFYING

Have students create a new Foldable titled "Pollution and Health." Have them label the tabs "Home," "School," and "Community." Ask them to analyze these three environments in terms of pollution and health and write their comments under the tabs.

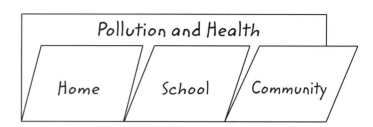

PROBLEM SOLVING

Have students make a new Foldable titled "Protect the Environment." Have them label the tabs "Reduce," "Reuse," and "Recycle" and record the main ideas on each topic under the tabs. Suggest that they organize a fundraiser or workday to help solve a specific pollution problem in their community.

Student Study Tip

Some students may become anxious when asked to make a presentation. Provide them with the following tips to help them prepare.

1. Evaluate your audience. How much do they already know about your subject?
2. Prepare an outline of the information you want to cover. Give background information or an overview first.
3. If applicable, plan to give a demonstration of some kind. It will help your audience understand the topic better.
4. At the end, summarize your main points.
5. When you've finished, address any questions.

Course 3

FOLDABLES

Notes

Notes

Notes

Notes

Notes

Notes

Notes

Notes

Notes

Notes

Notes